Senior Authors
Albert J. Harris
Mae Knight Clark

SHINING BRIDGES

Books are bridges,

Shining, free,

Which link us to

Ourselves-to-be.

"Golden Spurs," *by Virginia Scott Miner*

Josephine L. Wright

SHINING
BRIDGES

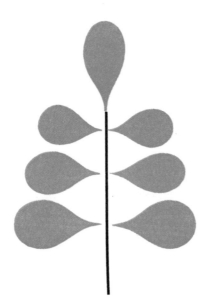

CALIFORNIA STATE SERIES
Published by
CALIFORNIA STATE DEPARTMENT OF EDUCATION
Sacramento, 1969

The Macmillan Company, New York
Collier-Macmillan Canada, Ltd., Toronto, Ontario
Printed in the United States of America

Illustrated by

Eric Carle, Les Goldstein, Charles Mikolaycak, George Porter, William Suttles

Grateful acknowledgment is made to Bernice Frankel for research and the adaptation of many stories in this volume.

Grateful acknowledgment is made to the following authors and publishers for permission to use copyrighted material:

Boy Scouts of America, for "What To Do If You Get Lost," adapted from "Strayed from the Gang" from *The Boy Scout Handbook*, copyright 1961, National Council, Boy Scouts of America.

Coward-McCann, Inc., for "Nothing at All," adapted from *Nothing at All* by Wanda Gag, copyright 1941 by Wanda Gag, and reprinted by permission of Coward-McCann, Inc.

Curtis Brown, Ltd., for "Jonathan Bing" by Beatrice Curtis Brown, reprinted by permission of the author, copyright © 1936 by Beatrice Curtis Brown.

Doubleday & Company, Inc., for "Roger and the Fox," adapted from *Roger and the Fox* by Lavinia R. Davis, copyright 1947 by Lavinia R. Davis, reprinted by permission of Doubleday & Company, Inc.

Doubleday & Company, Inc. and Harold Matson Company, Inc., for "Can Animals Learn to Talk?", adapted from *Man and Dolphin* by John C. Lilly, copyright © 1961 by John C. Lilly, reprinted by permission of Doubleday & Company, Inc., and in the British Commonwealth by permission of Harold Matson Company, Inc.

E. P. Dutton & Co., for "The Pirate Cook," copyright 1941 by Marchette Chute, from the book *Around and About* by Marchette Chute, published 1957 by E. P. Dutton & Co., Inc. and reprinted with their permission.

Contents

It Was Up to Them

7

Can You Believe It?

The World Around Us

10

Surprising Things Happen

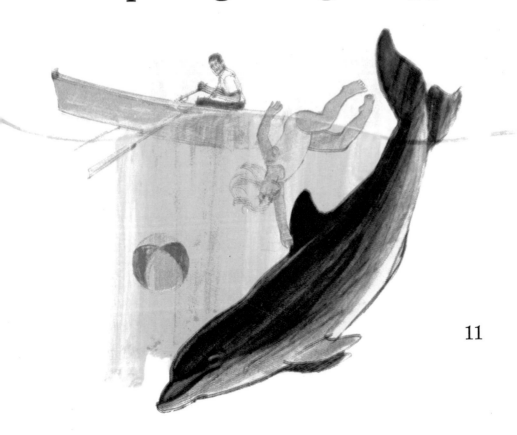

11

Eddie Needs a Doll

On his way to school, Eddie stopped to read something in a store window. His eyes grew big as he read: **Will give this printing press to anyone who will take it away.**

A real printing press! Eddie could hardly believe it.

"A printing press of my very own!" thought Eddie. "Now I can print a newspaper. I can sell it to everyone."

Eddie began to think about a name for his newspaper. By the time he got to school, he had one, **Hot News.**

12

Adapted from *Eddie and His Big Deals* by Carolyn Haywood, copyright © 1955 by Carolyn Haywood, by permission of William Morrow and Company, Inc.

All day Eddie thought about the printing press. That night he and his father went to get it.

"You are just a little late," said the man who was giving it away. "I gave it to a girl."

What could Eddie do now? He had to have that printing press! "Maybe I can buy it from the girl," he thought.

Eddie soon found out who had the printing press. It was Annie Pat. Eddie knew Annie Pat well. He tried to get the printing press from her, but she wouldn't let him have it. "You can use it here at my house," she said.

Every day Eddie went to Annie Pat's house to use the printing press. He hardly took time to go home to eat and sleep.

"I want to print at home," Eddie told Annie Pat. "If I find a doll for you, will you give me the printing press?"

"Well, **maybe,**" said Annie Pat. "Maybe if the doll is pretty enough, I will."

Eddie just had to find a doll. It had to be a doll pretty enough for Annie Pat.

Eddie knew about a store on High Street that had old things to sell. The money for the things went to people who needed help. Nearly anything could be found there.

Eddie went to that store. In the back of it were many old toys. Sitting on top of the toys was a doll. She had a big hole in the top of her head. She was far from clean. "Would a wig and a washing and new clothes make her pretty? Maybe," thought Eddie.

He went up to one of the workers in the store. "I know you don't start selling until tomorrow," he said. "Please, couldn't I just buy that doll over there? Couldn't I?"

"You are a dear," said the woman. She turned to her helpers. "Should we let this dear boy buy that doll for his sister?"

"Oh, yes, do let him," said the others.

Eddie gave the woman ten cents for the doll. "Could you tie it up in paper?" he asked.

"Oh no!" she answered. "We haven't any string or paper yet."

"All right," said Eddie, but he felt silly as he picked up the big doll. He didn't want anyone to see him with it.

15

What to Do Now

Eddie opened the door and looked up and down the street. There was no one in sight, so he went outside.

"The side streets will be better," he thought. He turned into a side street. What he saw made him stop so fast that he almost fell down. Two boys were playing ball there.

Back to High Street ran Eddie. That didn't help. On High Street he found three boys coming his way!

Eddie put the doll down at a newspaper stand and walked on. When the three boys went by him, Eddie was looking in a toy store window. Eddie made believe that he was thinking very hard about something in the window.

Eddie made believe so well that he didn't see a dog come down the street. The dog picked up the doll and ran off with it.

At last the boys were out of sight. Eddie went back to the newspaper stand for the doll. The doll was gone!

"Maybe I have forgotten where I left it," thought Eddie. He looked in all the stores along the street. No doll!

Two streets away Eddie saw something on the sidewalk. It looked like the doll. He hurried up the street.

It was the doll, all right, but a man got there before Eddie did. Eddie saw him bend down and pick up the doll.

The man looked around. He saw a baby carriage outside a store. The man put the doll into the baby carriage and walked on.

When Eddie ran up to the carriage, he saw a baby in it. The baby took hold of the doll's clothes. Eddie, too, took hold of the clothes. The baby yelled. Eddie pulled. The baby yelled harder than ever.

The door of the store opened. Out came a woman with a lot of packages. She looked at Eddie and the baby. "You bad boy!" she said. "A big boy like you, taking a doll away from a baby!"

"It's my doll," said Eddie.

"Oh, so you play with dolls, do you?" said the woman. She hurried on her way.

Just then the door opened again. Another woman came out. She looked at the doll in the carriage. Her eyes grew big. She pulled the doll away from the baby. Then she turned to Eddie.

"What do you mean by putting that dirty doll in my baby's carriage?" she shouted.

She pushed the doll into Eddie's hands. Then off she went with the crying baby.

19

Eddie Finds a Bag

Eddie stood holding the doll. "If only I could get a paper bag!" he thought.

He looked through the door of the store. There were lots of people inside, but Eddie **had** to get a bag. He held the doll back of him and went inside quickly.

Eddie went up to a man who was bending over a counter of cherries. "Would you please give me a paper bag?" he asked.

Without looking up, the man put his hand under the counter. He handed Eddie a paper bag. It was a very small bag. Only the doll's head would have gone into it.

"I need a bigger one," said Eddie.

"Well, help yourself," said the man.

Eddie dropped the doll on top of the cherry counter. Bending down, he began to look through the paper bags. He found lots of little bags, but no big ones.

Eddie went on looking through the bags. Then he heard the storekeeper say, "Who left this doll baby on top of the cherries?"

20

Eddie looked around. There stood the storekeeper with the doll in his hand. He was holding it up high. Everyone in the store was watching him.

Eddie could feel his face turning red. He went on looking for a big bag. Then he heard the storekeeper again.

"Children are always going off without their toys," said the storekeeper. "A doll baby in the cherries! The other day it was a fire truck on the meat counter." Then he called out to his helper, "Bill, if **anyone** comes back for this, it's up here."

21

Just then Eddie found a big paper bag. He looked up. There sat the doll on the very top shelf! She was pushed in with cans of cat meat and bottles of pop!

"Boy, did you get your bag?" asked the storekeeper.

"Yes, I found one," said Eddie. "Thanks."

"Well, goodby!" said the storekeeper.

Eddie didn't go. He kept standing there.

"Do you want something more?" asked the man.

Eddie looked up at the top shelf. "I . . . I'm just looking," he said.

"Did you forget what your mother told you to buy?" asked the storekeeper.

"Uh," said Eddie. "Uh—how much is a small bag of cherries?"

"Ten cents," said the storekeeper.

22

The Right Time at Last

Eddie bought the cherries and went outside. He stood at the door and ate the cherries. He watched the people go in and out of the door. He was waiting for a time when no one was in the store. At last that time came! Eddie ran into the store.

"You back again?" asked the storekeeper. "Did you forget something?"

Before Eddie could answer, the door opened and two big boys came into the store. The boys were friends of Eddie's brother. They waved to Eddie, and he waved back.

The storekeeper was looking down into Eddie's face. "Hurry up, boy. What do you want to buy?" he asked.

"Well . . . uh . . . I'll have some cupcakes." The cupcakes were ten cents. Eddie bought them and went outside. He stood near the door and ate the cupcakes. He had bought so much. "What more?" he asked himself. "I have only five cents left."

In and out, in and out of the door went the people. Eddie watched them while he ate his cupcakes. At last there came another time when no one was in the store.

24

Eddie went through the door like a rocket. "Please," he said to the man. "Will you hand me that doll off the shelf? It's my doll. Can I have it quickly, please?"

The storekeeper looked very surprised. He took the doll down. He laughed as he handed it to Eddie. "Why didn't you say so before?" he asked.

Eddie pushed the doll into the big paper bag. "I couldn't," he said. "I didn't want people to think it was my doll. I bought it for a girl. I don't like dolls!"

Eddie ran out of the store. He hurried all the way home. Finding a doll had been hard. Getting it home had been even harder! Never had Eddie been so glad to open his own door.

Eddie washed the doll's face. He got a wig for the doll. His mother made clothes for it.

"Do you think Annie Pat will like it now?" asked Eddie's mother.

Eddie looked at the doll. "You mean that's the doll I bought for ten cents?" he asked. In her shiny white dress and blue velvet coat, the doll looked like a fairy.

"Oh, Mother!" said Eddie. "She's pretty!"

When Eddie took the doll to Annie Pat, she rubbed her eyes. "You mean you are giving this to me?" she cried. "Oh, Eddie. She's not just pretty—she's beautiful!"

Eddie got his printing press at last.

Little Jonathan

Little Jonathan Brown lived a long time ago. He had many brothers and sisters. All of them were much older and bigger than he was.

"You're too little to ride a horse," they told Jonathan. "You're too little to cook meat over a fire." Too little for this. Too little for that. Jonathan was tired of being too little to do the things he wanted to do.

27

Adapted with permission of The Macmillan Company and Miriam E. Mason from *Little Jonathan* by Miriam E. Mason. Copyright 1944 by The Macmillan Company.

One day a friend of the Browns gave them some buckskin. Jonathan's mother made Jonathan a coat and pants out of the buckskin.

At first the new clothes were very big on Jonathan. As time went on, they were not quite so big. Jonathan could tell that he was growing. Still, he was not growing as fast as he wished. He was still too little to do all the things he wanted to do.

At last one day, Jonathan was asked to do something important. The Browns were going to have a get-together at their house. They sent Jonathan to ask everyone to come to it. For this important day, Jonathan wore his buckskin clothes.

Jonathan walked three miles. He knocked at the door of every house. He told everyone the day and time of the get-together and asked them to come.

When he was through he was hot and tired. On the trail home he came to Honey Spring. Honey Spring was a lovely spot. The cold water was always running and it made a quiet round pool. Jonathan stood and looked at himself in the water.

"I wish I were bigger!" he said. All at once he thought of something he had heard long ago. "Honey Spring is magic," his sister had said. "Dip your hand into the pool three times. Make a wish as you do it. You will get your wish."

"I wonder if that is so," thought Jonathan. His sister had wished to grow tall and pretty. Now she **was** tall and pretty. "It wouldn't hurt to try," he thought.

Jonathan stretched way out over the quiet pool and went dip, dip, dip. He stretched too far. "O-o-o-o-o-o-!" cried Jonathan. He fell right into the pool. Up to his ears he fell!

Jonathan got out of the water all right. But he couldn't get the water out of his buckskin clothes. Well, the sun would dry them, he thought. Jonathan stretched out in the sun and fell asleep.

He had forgotten about his wish.

Big Jonathan

Jonathan woke up as the sun was about to go down. "I must hurry home!" he thought. "It will soon be night."

He sat up and stretched. He could hardly put his arms up. He stood up. His legs felt funny, too. He looked down.

"My goodness!" said Jonathan out loud. His legs had grown much too long for his pants. Now his pants didn't even begin to cover them. He looked at his arms. They had grown much too long for his coat.

"My goodness!" said Jonathan again. "What happened? How long did I sleep?" Then he thought—"Oh, the magic spring! I'm getting my wish!"

Jonathan started home. He had more than a mile to go. His clothes were so tight he could hardly walk. "How long will I keep growing?" he wondered.

He wanted to hurry, but he couldn't with such tight clothes. He wondered how big he really was.

He stretched up his arms, and oh, my! His arms popped right through his coat! "Soon I will pop right out of my clothes," thought Jonathan. He laughed to himself. "By now I must be as tall as my tallest brother! Maybe I'm even taller!"

He took a long jump and the legs of his pants popped open!

"How surprised Mother and the girls will be when I come through the door!" he laughed. "If I keep on growing, maybe I won't be able to get through the door."

This thought gave him a strange feeling. It didn't seem funny, now.

"I wonder where I will sleep," he whispered to himself. He thought of his little bed. "I can never sleep in it again!"

How strange it would be to look down at everybody. He had always looked up at them before. How strange when he couldn't get through the door without bending!

34

Things to Think About

"I will be big enough to hold a horse in my arms," thought Jonathan. He tried to laugh, but he didn't feel like laughing.

"A kitten is better to hold than a horse," he thought. "Maybe I am getting too big."

Soon he felt tears running down his face. "I wish I hadn't made that wish!" he said.

He tried to hurry home before he got any bigger. He couldn't hurry. His clothes were too tight. "I must be huge," he thought.

As he walked along the trail he had a new thought. What if everybody were afraid of him? What if his sisters ran away, yelling? What if his mother went into the cellar and locked the door?

At last he came in sight of the house. It was almost dark now. The smell of something cooking came from the kitchen. It smelled good. Jonathan felt hungry.

"I wonder where I'll eat tonight," he whispered to himself. "There will not be a chair big enough for me."

He went up the trail to the kitchen door. It was open.

"I'll bend way down and maybe I can get through the door," he whispered to himself. Bend he did, and he got through the kitchen door. He was not too huge for that.

His mother and sisters were in the kitchen. "Don't be afraid!" he called loudly. "It's only Jonathan. I won't hurt you!"

It was such a surprise for Jonathan when his sisters laughed. He rubbed his eyes hard and looked at them. They were not little. They were still much bigger and taller than he was!

"What has happened to you?" they asked.

Jonathan told about Honey Spring. He told how he had fallen into it and grown big.

His mother laughed and took him in her arms. "My poor little Jonathan!" she said. "You have not grown any bigger. Your clothes have grown smaller. Buckskin gets smaller when it's wet. That's why your clothes are tight."

Jonathan looked about the quiet kitchen. He looked up at his mother. "You mean I'm still little Jonathan!" he whispered.

"You're still little Jonathan," said his mother. "I'm glad you are!"

Jonathan curled up in his mother's arms. There was his little chair, still just right for him. In the bedroom was his bed, still just right. There were his big sisters, with such pretty smiles.

It was not so bad, after all, to be little. Just little Jonathan Brown!

Sizes

If you were as big as a giant flea,
How much would you have to grow to be
The size of the tiniest head-to-tail
Very most midgety baby whale?

I mean to say—and it's no surprise—
Whatever you do about your size,
There's always something a size or two
Very much bigger or smaller than you.

I mean to say, what's big of some
Is small of others. Now get along home.
And whether you stay or wander far,
Be just the size of whatever you are.

John Ciardi

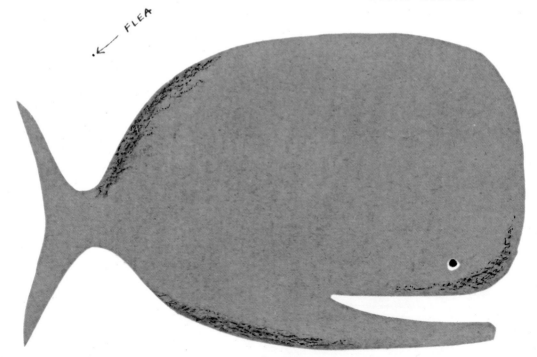

Lost in the Woods

Johnny was a real boy who lived a long, long time ago. At that time there were many Indians where he lived. Some of the Indians were friendly but some were not.

Johnny lived near a big woods. There were many animals in the woods. Johnny knew that some animals could hurt him. He knew better than to go into the woods alone. The little dog, Trojan, knew better, too.

One day Johnny saw Trojan run by, with his nose to the ground. He seemed to be on the trail of something, maybe a rabbit. He was heading straight for the woods!

39

Adapted with permission of the author and publisher from *First Adventure* by Elizabeth Coatsworth. Copyright 1950 by The Macmillan Company.

"Trojan! Come back!" called Johnny. "You know we mustn't go into the woods!"

Trojan knew, but he went into the woods anyway.

Johnny didn't know what to do. The little dog was almost sure to be killed by a wolf. Johnny didn't want that to happen. "Maybe just this once I can go a little way into the woods," he thought. "Then I can catch Trojan and bring him back."

Johnny hurried after Trojan, calling to him as he ran. Trojan turned his head and looked back at Johnny. His eyes were bright and shiny. He was glad Johnny was coming along with him. He kept on running, but not fast enough to get out of sight.

40

Johnny was getting tired when they came to a place where blueberries were growing. He stopped, and so did Trojan. Johnny picked some berries. He gave one to Trojan. Trojan only smelled it and turned his head away.

"That means more for me," said Johnny. He sat down and ate the berries. By the time he had all he wanted, it was beginning to get dark.

"Come along, boy," Johnny said, getting up. Trojan barked and wagged his tail. They started up the hill, the way they had come.

41

They walked and they walked. Things didn't look the same, now that it was getting dark. The trees didn't look the same. The trail didn't look the same. The more they walked, the stranger things looked.

They made their way down another hillside. They came to a stream of water which they had never seen before.

"We are lost," whispered Johnny. He felt scared. His gray eyes grew bigger and he wondered what to do. He had not wanted to go into the woods. He had just wanted to catch Trojan.

42

Trojan didn't seem to know they were lost. He wagged his tail and took a drink from the stream. Johnny made a cup with his hands and took a drink of water, too. As he was drinking, he had a new thought.

"Go home, Trojan!" he said. "Home!"

The dog just wagged his tail. He was having such fun where he was. Or maybe he was lost, too. Anyway, he was no help.

Johnny started off again. It was getting so dark that he could hardly see his way. He was getting hungry and tired. He wished he were home with his father and mother.

"Who-who-who!" called an owl.

Johnny began to cry. He cried for quite a while. Then he said to himself, "What good does crying do? I won't cry any more."

Noises in the Night

"Father will come and find us tonight," Johnny told Trojan. Trojan was walking very close to Johnny now.

"Who-who-who!" went the owl again.

"Who-who-who!" answered another owl.

Something ran by Johnny's feet. Something jumped in a tree. Something flew close to his head. Johnny didn't know where he was going, but he was so afraid that he hurried on. It was night now. He could see stars through the branches.

Then the loud noise of a gun came through the quiet night.

"Maybe that's Father's gun!" Johnny said.

Johnny listened. Where had that gun shot come from? He didn't know. He shouted and shouted. The owls stopped who-ing to listen. The animals stopped running to listen. The trees seemed to be listening, too.

The man with the gun didn't hear the little boy calling. He was too far away.

Johnny shouted until he couldn't shout any more. Then he stood there, with Trojan close by him. He listened for another gun shot. This time he didn't hear a gun shot. He heard the howl of a wolf.

Johnny looked for a tree with branches that he could climb. But what about Trojan? He couldn't climb.

The wolf howled again. The howl seemed a little nearer.

Johnny sat down at the foot of a tree. Trojan gave a little bark and curled up close to him. The dog seemed even more scared than Johnny. Johnny put his arms around him. "Don't be afraid, Trojan. You're all right," he whispered. "I'll take care of you tonight."

Maybe the wolf didn't know that such a little boy and a dog were lost in his woods. Anyway, he didn't come any nearer. Johnny didn't hear any more howls. He didn't hear any more gun shots, either. He and Trojan fell asleep.

46

The next morning the sun was bright when Johnny woke up. He heard a bird singing. It was fun to be in the woods. What a story he would have to tell his mother and father! Now that it was light he was sure he could find his way home.

Johnny found some more blueberries and ate them. Then he and Trojan walked on through the woods. They walked all day but they didn't find their way home.

That night they curled up together under a shelf of rock. They soon fell asleep. They were not afraid that night. They were getting used to sleeping in the woods.

47

Tired and Hungry

The third day Johnny woke up and looked around.

"Home must be down there," he said. His feet hurt from climbing over the rocks, and his head felt strange. "Maybe we will never get home," he whispered to himself. He didn't say it to Trojan, though. He had to take care of Trojan.

They didn't find much to eat that day. The sun was hot and the trail was rocky. Johnny and Trojan were so tired, they went to sleep long before dark.

The fourth day Johnny didn't walk very straight. Trojan had hurt a foot on a rock. He was walking on only three legs.

48

That day they found a rabbit that had been killed. A wolf had eaten most of it. There was still a little meat on the bones. At last Trojan had something to eat. Johnny took one bite, but he wasn't **that** hungry.

All that day they climbed up a hill. When the sun went down Johnny made a bed of branches. He and Trojan were soon fast asleep.

That night a bear came near and looked at them. Trojan was so tired that he didn't know the bear was there. The bear just stood there watching Trojan and Johnny, then went on his way.

On the fifth day they climbed up on a high rock. There they could look out for many miles over blue sea and green woods.

Johnny and Trojan were very, very hungry and tired. They went to sleep for a while that morning. When Johnny woke up he couldn't walk. He got down on all fours to go down the hill. Then he found a straight branch and used it to help himself walk.

"Let's go down there, Trojan. We may find water to drink," said Johnny.

Trojan wagged his tail and looked up into Johnny's face. The dog's coat was covered with dirt. He didn't bark any more. The shine had gone out of his eyes. He still wagged his tail whenever Johnny talked to him, though.

The Smoke

They were almost at the foot of the hill, when Johnny saw smoke. Then it seemed as though there was no smoke. He stopped and rubbed his eyes. There was the smoke again! It was streaming up into the air.

"Smoke," whispered Johnny. "People must live down there. They will help us." He began to hurry. He tripped. He fell. He got up and went on.

They came to a beaten trail, like the trails near his home. They heard people talking. Johnny was almost running.

They came to the end of the woods. There were the people, picking corn! They were Indians.

51

An Indian woman saw Johnny. She dropped the corn she was holding and picked up the little boy. She held him close in her arms.

The woman hurried with Johnny to her home. She gave him soup. She didn't forget Trojan, either. She gave him a bone with meat on it.

Many of the Indians had never seen a white boy before. They came close and looked at Johnny. They were surprised by his gray eyes and white skin. They had never seen clothes like he was wearing, either. They felt his soft white skin and his clothes.

Johnny didn't understand what the Indians said. He knew only one Indian word—Squanto. Squanto was the name of an Indian who lived right near Johnny. "Maybe these Indians know Squanto, too," thought Johnny. "Do you know Squanto?" he asked the tallest Indian.

"Squanto?" said the tallest Indian. He turned and said something to the other Indians. "Squanto!" said one of them, with a smile. He said it as if he knew Squanto.

Everybody was very kind to Johnny that night. The next day they talked and talked about him. On the second morning they gave Johnny some Indian clothes and toys. Then two of the Indians took Johnny and Trojan into a boat, and the others waved goodby.

"The Indians must be taking me home," thought Johnny. They went many miles in two days. On the first day they made a stop just to sleep on land. On the second day, though, they made a stop where they stayed a week.

At the place where they were staying Johnny met many Indians. They, too, wondered at his white skin and strange clothes. Some gave him buckskin clothes, others took him fishing in a little stream. All were very kind to Johnny. They were kind to Trojan, too. They didn't let their dogs fight with Johnny's dog.

The week went by quickly for Johnny.

Johnny learned to like living with the Indians. He missed his father and mother, though. He wanted so much to see them. One day Johnny was playing with some Indian children. All at once he looked up and there was Squanto, his Indian friend from home!

"Hello, Johnny," said Squanto. "I heard that you were here and came quickly. I came on a friend's ship to take you home."

"Home!" said Johnny. "Oh, Squanto, thank you! I like living here, but I miss my mother and father. What stories I have to tell them! I can hardly wait!"

Then Johnny turned to his Indian friends. He would never forget how kind they had been to him. With tears in his eyes he said goodby to them. Then Squanto picked him up and took him out to the ship.

"Come on, Trojan," called Johnny. "You can swim out."

On the ship Johnny put his arms around Trojan. Johnny's eyes were bright and shiny. "Trojan," he said, "you're going home at last."

Trojan's eyes began to shine. He jumped up and barked. Trojan knew the meaning of "home."

What to Do If You Get Lost

If you go into the woods with friends who
are older than you are, stay with them. If
you don't, you may get lost. If you **do** get
lost, though, this is what you should do.

Sit down and stay where you are. Don't
try to find your friends—let **them** find **you.**
You can help them to find you by staying
in one place.

There is another way you can help your
friends or other nearby people to find you.
Give them a signal by shouting or whistling
three times. Stop. Then shout or whistle
three times again. Any signal given three
times is a call for help.

Keep up the shouting or whistling, always three times together. Then the people who hear you will know that you are not just making noise for fun. They will let you know that they have heard your signal. They will give two shouts, two whistles, or two gun shots. Whenever a signal is given twice it is an answer to a call for help.

If you don't think that you will be found before night comes, get some branches. Try to put them together so that they make a little house. Cover up the holes with branches that have lots of leaves. Make yourself a soft bed with leaves and grass.

What should you do if you get hungry or need drinking water? You would have to leave your little branch house to look for a stream. Don't just walk away. Make a trail for yourself so you can find your way back. Do this by picking off small branches and dropping them as you walk.

The most important thing to do when you are lost is—stay in one place.

58

In Other Places

Now you know what to do if you get lost in the woods. You should also know what to do if you get lost in other places. First of all, be sure that you know your name, address, and telephone number.

If you get lost from your mother on the street, don't walk around trying to find her. Stay right where you are and see if a policeman is nearby. If you see a policeman, go up to him and ask him to help you. Tell him your name, address, and telephone number. Then he will either find your mother or take you home.

If you don't see a policeman, go into a store. Ask someone who works in the store to help you.

Some very big stores have a loudspeaker. It makes a voice loud enough to be heard by everybody in the store.

If you get lost in a very big store, look for someone who works at a counter. Ask to have your mother called through the loudspeaker. If your mother hears the voice, she will come straight to you.

If you get lost at a beach, see if there is a policeman close by. If there isn't, see if there is a lifeguard. There are lifeguards at many beaches. Ask the lifeguard to telephone a policeman. When the policeman comes, he will help you.

A storekeeper or a man who sells things at a stand will call a policeman for you, too. It is best to ask someone who is working at the beach to help you.

If you get lost in a park, first see if there is a policeman nearby. If there isn't, look for a man who is selling something in the park. Ask him for help.

Don't forget the most important thing to do. Stay close to the place where you first knew you were lost.

In most places the things to do if you get lost are the same. Don't walk around trying to find your mother or friends. Do ask for help from a nearby policeman, storekeeper, or standkeeper. Just do these things, and soon you won't be lost any more.

Jane and the Dolphin

Jane Turner lived in a small hotel right on the beach. Her mother and father owned the hotel, and Jane was glad they did. People came there with their children, and the children became Jane's friends. They went swimming with her almost every day.

63

One of Jane's friends was a boy named Billy. One day Jane and Billy were playing with a beach ball, and Billy got hurt. The beach ball hit him on the mouth. For a second Billy was angry. He threw the ball so hard that it went way out over the water.

Then a strange thing happened. As Jane and Billy watched, a big dark animal jumped out of the water. It tried to catch the ball on its nose!

"That's a dolphin!" cried Jane. "It looks just like one I saw in a picture!"

There was just one thing Billy wanted to know. "Do dolphins bite?" he asked.

Jane looked at Billy and laughed. "Oh, Billy, no!" she said. "Dolphins don't bite. They just play. Daddy told me about them."

Just then the dolphin began to nose the ball nearer to Jane and Billy. As it swam it opened its mouth.

"Just look at its teeth!" howled Billy. He began to run to the beach, yelling, "Help! Help!" Jane knew she shouldn't be scared but she was. She ran, too.

Everybody on the beach saw the big animal. Everybody started shouting at once. A number of people ran out to get Jane and Billy. A big man picked them up and hurried away from the swimming dolphin.

The dolphin stayed a distance away, but it swam nearer the beach. It nosed the beach ball almost all the way to the beach. It opened its mouth and showed all its teeth. Everybody was glad when it swam away.

65

Jane did what she always did when she
was afraid. She ran to her father and curled
up in his arms. "Daddy," she cried, "a dolphin
is in the water!"

Mr. Turner held Jane close and talked to
her quietly. "Now, Jane," he said, "dolphins
don't hurt people. They like people. I have
told you that many times."

"I know," said Jane. "I wasn't scared
until he swam toward us with his mouth
open. Daddy, he has such a lot of teeth. I
just can't help being afraid. Everybody else
is afraid, too."

"You're right, we're afraid!" said a woman's loud voice. Jane and her father looked up. In the door stood Mrs. Inman and many other people from the hotel. They all wanted to talk to Mr. Turner right away.

"We came here to swim," said Mrs. Inman. "Our children want to swim, too. We're afraid to swim with that dolphin around. It went away but it might come back. We're going to leave this village and go somewhere else."

That night nearly all of the people at the hotel packed their bags and left.

"This is bad for us and for all the other villagers," said Mr. Turner. "The storekeepers sell their things to the people who stay at our hotel. The storekeepers need the money the people give them, just as we do. If the people don't come back—"

"Yes, Daddy, go on," said Jane.

Mr. Turner looked at Mrs. Turner. "You tell her, dear," he said to his wife.

Mrs. Turner put her arm around Jane. "Jane," she said. "If the summer people don't come back, it will be hard for all of us. One bad summer might make us have to give up this hotel and move away. I don't know what the villagers would do without a hotel here. It would be too bad, but we might have to move."

Jane went to sleep feeling very sad.

Getting Rid of the Dolphin

Two long weeks went by and only one man came to the Turners' hotel. The dolphin came to the Turners' beach, though. He came every day and played in the waves near the beach.

"Go away!" shouted Mrs. Turner. She threw a beach ring at the dolphin. The dolphin caught it and swam around with it on his nose.

"Go away!" yelled Mr. Turner. He threw a beach ball at the dolphin. The dolphin caught it and nosed it back toward him.

"That does it," said Mr. Turner quietly. "I'm just going to have to get rid of him." He hurried into the hotel. When he came back he had something in his hand. He put it into the boat. It was a gun.

"No, Daddy, no! Don't kill the dolphin!" cried Jane. She climbed into the boat just as her father started off. "Daddy, I like the dolphin now!" she shouted. She jumped up and just then a big wave rocked the boat. It rocked Jane right into the water.

Before Jane knew what was happening, the dolphin was swimming under her. He pushed her up and then began to move her toward the beach.

Jane looked at the big playful animal and laughed. "Did you think I was drowning?" she asked. Then she swam away to the boat.

70

"He would make a good lifeguard," she told her father. "He tried to save me from drowning. I'm going to call him Smiley. He always looks as if he has a smile on his face."

"Not when he shows his teeth and scares people," said Mr. Turner. "Jane, try to understand. I **must** get rid of him or else we might have to give up our hotel."

"I **do** understand," cried Jane, "but listen, Daddy. I have a plan! I just want you to wait three weeks so I can try it. Please!"

"I'll wait **one** week," said her father.

"All right," Jane answered. To herself she whispered, "One week! It will be impossible to do it in one week! Oh, Smiley, I don't think I can save you, after all! I'll try, though, Smiley. I'll try."

The Impossible Plan

That afternoon Jane took a beach ball and a whistle to the beach. It was the whistle she used to call her dog. She waited a long time for Smiley to come. When at last she saw him she blew the whistle. Then she threw the ball.

How that animal loved to play! He jumped out of the water. He made a whistling sound and came down on the ball. He pressed the ball deep into the sea. When the ball came up, it shot high into the air. He waited for it to come down and he caught it.

Then Jane threw a hoop to Smiley. He liked to play with the hoop as much as he liked to play with the ball.

72

After a while Smiley nosed the ball back toward Jane. He kept a distance away, though. Jane wasn't afraid of Smiley, but Smiley was still just a little afraid of Jane.

The second day Jane didn't have to wait for Smiley. She just blew the whistle and he swam right over to play. This time he didn't keep quite such a big distance between himself and Jane.

On the third day Smiley swam side by side with Jane. The fourth day Jane stretched out her hand and tried to stroke him. Smiley made a whistling sound and jumped away. He came back, though, and Jane tried to stroke him again. This time Smiley didn't jump away. "See?" said Jane. "My hand feels good on your skin."

Smiley made a sound like a creaking door.

"Does the creaking-door sound mean yes?" asked Jane. It seemed to, for Smiley did let Jane stroke him.

Smiley didn't want to play ball on the fifth day. He didn't want to swim, either. He just wanted to stand still and be stroked!

Smiley's skin had a pretty shine to it in the sun. Jane rubbed him all over, from head to tail, until she was tired. Smiley wasn't tired, though. He wasn't playful, either. Instead, he gave a creaking-door sound and turned on his side. Jane had to start petting him all over again.

That afternoon Smiley swam between Jane's legs and came up with her on his back. He took her for little rides all that day. Sometimes Jane held on to him instead of riding on his back. That way she got a ride whenever she wanted one.

Jane Gets Help

The next morning when Jane came to see Smiley, a tall man was with her. "Smiley, this is Mr. Patrick," said Jane. "Mr. Patrick works for a newspaper. He's going to take a picture of you and write a story about you. Then no one will be afraid of you any more."

Smiley made a whistling sound through his blowhole. Jane threw the beach ball to him and he caught it. He hit it up into the air with his tail and caught it again and again. Then he nosed the ball to Jane and took her for a ride. After that he made the creaking-door sound and turned on his side to be petted. He let the man from the newspaper pet him, too.

75

"What a story this will make!" said Mr. Patrick. He took many pictures of Smiley and Jane, then hurried away.

That very afternoon some of the pictures were printed in the newspaper. Mr. and Mrs. Turner were surprised when they saw them.

"So that's what you have been up to, Jane!" said Mr. Turner. He didn't have time to say anything more, for many people came hurrying in.

First to come through the door was—of all people!—Mrs. Inman. She wasn't angry today. Instead, she was very friendly. "When will Smiley come to the beach?" she asked. "My little boy wants to pet him."

"He will come when I whistle," said Jane. She went outside and what she saw made her stop in surprise!

The parking space was full of cars as far as she could see! The beach was full of people, all looking for Smiley!

That is what happened on the first day. On the second day even more people came. It was almost impossible to find parking space. They kept coming all that week, and the next and next. For the very first time every room in the Turner hotel was full.

Many newspapers printed pictures and stories about the playful dolphin. People came hundreds of miles to see him. To make room for the people the little village had to grow into a town.

All this happened because a little girl worked out what seemed an impossible plan.

Summer Song

By the sand between my toes,
By the waves behind my ears,
By the sunburn on my nose,
By the little salty tears
That make rainbows in the sun
When I squeeze my eyes and run,
By the way the seagulls screech,
Guess where I am? *At the* . . . . . !
By the way the children shout
Guess what happened? *School is* . . . !
By the way I sing this song
Guess if summer lasts too long:
You must answer Right or . . . . . !

John Ciardi

Can Animals Learn to Talk?

Do you know what is one of the biggest adventures anyone can have? It is to find out something that no one else knew before.

Finding out that the earth is round was a big adventure. Finding out that we can fly like birds in an airplane was an adventure, too. Finding out that we can rocket into space was another big adventure.

Some of the people who work trying to find out new things are called scientists.

79

Based on facts from *Man and Dolphin* by John C. Lilly, M. D., copyright © 1961, by permission of Dr. Lilly and the Communication Research Institute, Coconut Grove, Florida.

Scientists are going on many big adventures right now. One of them is an experiment that children like. Boys and girls have always wanted to talk to animals. Some day they may really be able to do it! Experiments are now being made to find out.

A scientist named Dr. John C. Lilly has made many such experiments. Mrs. Lilly has helped him. His children—three boys and three girls—have helped him, too.

Before Dr. Lilly began his experiments, he had to think about which animal to use. One animal stood out as being best—the dolphin.

What do we know about dolphins right now? One thing we know is that they sometimes help people. They have saved people from drowning by pushing them to land. They have helped people catch fish by making the fish swim toward the boats. One dolphin was well known because he met ships and swam along with them. Another liked to play at the beach with a certain little girl and her friends.

Dolphins are smart and learn quickly. They have been trained to come when they are called. They jump quite a distance out of the water when given a signal. They catch balls. They go after bits of paper that people throw to them. They like to have people rub their skin.

In some places they swim with strangers as well as with their trainers. People are sometimes scared when a dolphin swims toward them with his mouth open.

Dolphins will also go through their tricks for strangers. A trainer showed one of Dr. Lilly's children how to whistle and use hand signals. The boy then was able to get the dolphins to do their tricks.

Dolphins are very playful animals. Dr. Lilly tells of a trainer who wanted three dolphins to go through a hoop. He stood under the water behind the hoop holding a fish. One dolphin swam toward the hoop. A second one swam behind the trainer and helped himself to the fish. The third pushed the trainer's legs out from under him!

Do dolphins have a language of their own? Dr. Lilly believes that they may have a language with many words in it. If so, they can talk things over together, just as we can.

We are not yet sure about this. Dr. Lilly's experiments may help us find out.

Dr. Lilly tells about a dolphin that got hurt. It fell over on its right side. Its blowhole was under water, and it couldn't come up for air. It was about to drown, for dolphins need air just as we do.

The dolphin didn't drown, though. It whistled for help to the two other dolphins in the pool. They hurried right over. Quickly they pushed the dolphin's head up. Then he could take air through his blowhole.

The three dolphins made sounds as if they were talking about what to do! Then the two helpers took turns swimming along the right side of their hurt friend. They helped him to swim. They let him press down on them to come up for air. They had thought out a way to help him and they had used it.

Dr. Lilly saw dolphins save drowning friends in a number of ways. He says that each time the dolphins seemed to talk things over first.

Teaching a Dolphin to Talk

Dr. Lilly's experiments show that dolphins learn much faster than dogs or monkeys. He believes they might learn as fast as people!

Dr. Lilly also found out that dolphins can hear much higher sounds than we can. They also talk in much higher voices than ours. He says that he found out something else, too. Just as he was learning about dolphins, dolphins seemed to be learning about him!

One day Dr. Lilly was teaching a dolphin to whistle in a certain way. Each time the dolphin whistled, Dr. Lilly stroked him so that he liked it. Then, says Dr. Lilly, the dolphin made an experiment of his own.

Each whistle the dolphin gave was a little higher than the last one. At last Dr. Lilly couldn't hear the whistles at all. He knew that the dolphin was still whistling, though, because his blowhole moved.

When Dr. Lilly couldn't hear the whistles, he didn't stroke the dolphin. Then the dolphin whistled lower again. He had found out what sounds Dr. Lilly could hear. After that he kept his whistles low enough for Dr. Lilly to hear them.

How can you help a dolphin to learn our language—if he can learn it? Dr. Lilly believes you may help a dolphin to learn in the same way you help a baby to talk.

A mother is with her baby quite a bit. She pats him. She plays with him. She gives him food. She does many things to make her baby happy. As she does these things, she talks to her baby.

Hearing his mother talk helps the baby learn to talk. The more the mother talks, the more he tries to copy the sounds she makes. Talking is a good thing, the baby finds. Now he can tell his mother just what he wants.

Dr. Lilly believes that a dolphin trained in the same way might learn to talk. He thinks you must talk to the dolphin and let him hear the sounds you make. When the dolphin tries to copy the sounds, give him food. Play with him and rub his skin. Then the dolphin will learn that making sounds will get him the things he wants. He may learn to use some of our words to ask for food.

Dr. Lilly made a pool for dolphins. He bought a bottle-nosed dolphin which he named Elvar and kept him in the pool. He and his helpers go swimming with Elvar. They pet him. They play with him. They give him food. As they do these things for their bottle-nosed dolphin, they talk to him. They want to teach Elvar to copy the sounds of our language.

Dr. Lilly has two loudspeakers. One is an underwater loudspeaker. Through it Elvar can hear everything Dr. Lilly and his helpers say. The other is an air loudspeaker. Through that one Dr. Lilly and his helpers can listen to Elvar's sounds.

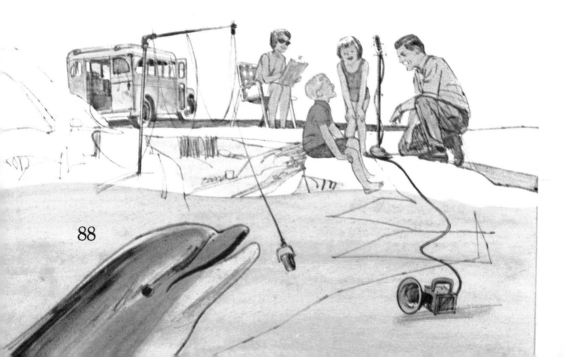

At first Dr. Lilly heard just whistles, creaking-door sounds, and other noises over the loudspeaker. Then one day he heard strange noises. They seemed to say, "Ha, ha, ha!" They sounded like children laughing. Elvar had just heard people laughing. Maybe he was copying their laugh!

Dr. Lilly put the sounds Elvar made on tapes. When he played these tapes back, he was surprised. In a high-voiced quacking way, Elvar seemed to be copying people! He seemed to be copying words he had heard Dr. Lilly say!

Dr. Lilly tells us of even more surprises. Dolphins talk much more quickly than we do, as well as in higher voices. Dr. Lilly played the dolphin tapes back more slowly. That made the voices sound lower. Then many more of the dolphin's quackings sounded like words!

Will boys and girls ever be able to talk to dolphins? Are dolphins as smart as people? Some day we may know about these things. Dr. Lilly and his helpers are going on the big adventure of trying to find out.

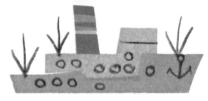

Sailor John

Young Stephen has a young friend John
Who in his years is getting on.
He's getting on for six, I think,
Or seven. Yes, he's on the brink
Of seven, which is pretty old
Unless you're eight or nine all told.
But anyhow, John has a notion
That he would like to sail the ocean.
He has the notion, understand,
But *not* the ocean—just the land.
John hasn't any boat as yet,
Although his feet are often wet:
They're wet today because of rain.
Quite right—he can't go out again
Unless he finds some other shoes.
John has a notion he will choose
To stay inside and shut the door
And lie right down upon the floor
And think about the ocean, how
It's not available just now;
And think about the kinds of boat
He doesn't have that wouldn't float.

David McCord

91

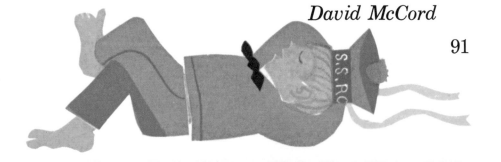

It Was Up to Them

The Boy Who Couldn't Swim

Tommy and his mother and father went to the country each summer. This summer they took a house right beside a lake.

"I'm so glad we're here," said Tommy. "I didn't learn how to swim last year, but **this** year I will. You wait and see."

"Good!" said his father. "I'm glad you want to learn now. Many of the boys and girls here don't know how to swim. We're getting a lifeguard to teach you. His name is Big Jim, and I'm sure you'll like him."

94

Tommy did like Big Jim. Just the same he couldn't do the things Big Jim asked him to do in the water.

The other children laughed at Tommy. "He's afraid of the water," they said. "Tommy is a baby! Tommy is a frightened baby!"

Tommy wasn't frightened. He just didn't like the feel of the water in his eyes and ears. He didn't like to put his head under water.

"Leave Tommy alone," said the lifeguard to the other children. "He'll learn to swim. He'll learn when he really wants to learn."

The next morning Tommy started for the lake. He found many things to look at and to think about. The next thing he knew he had walked around the lake. He didn't get into it at all that day.

That night at supper he told his father and mother about his walk. He told them, "I had such a good time today. I'll learn to swim tomorrow."

When tomorrow morning came, Tommy thought he would go straight to the lake. But on the way he found some bushes full of berries. He stopped to eat some. Then he heard a soft rustle under the bushes.

Tommy stood very still and listened. He heard the rustle again. He started to get down to look under the bushes. When he moved, a little squirrel jumped out. It ran off through the woods.

Tommy stared at it until it was out of sight. Then he walked on and on through the woods. He hoped he would see another squirrel. He had forgotten that he should be on his way to the lake to learn to swim.

When he got home he told about the squirrel. "You should have seen it run," he said. "Tomorrow I'll learn to swim."

So it went. Tommy always planned to learn to swim "tomorrow." Tomorrow always came and went, and Tommy still didn't learn to swim.

Too Late?

"Tomorrow I'll learn to swim," Tommy said one night at supper time. "I am really going to do it this time."

His father looked at him closely. "Tommy," he said. "I think it's too late for you to learn to swim now. The summer is almost over. In two weeks we'll be saying goodby to the country."

Tommy stared at his father. "Too late?" he cried. "Oh, Dad, I didn't mean to break my word." Tears came into Tommy's eyes.

"I know you didn't mean to break your word," said Father. "Tommy, do I see dirt on your hands? Why don't you go and wash up. Then you'll feel better."

Tommy hurried to his room. His father hadn't sent him out because of the dirt on his hands. He had sent him out because Tommy was about to cry and wanted to do it alone. Tommy's father was a very understanding man. He, too, had found it hard to learn to swim.

98

Tommy felt unhappy all night long. The next morning he went straight to the lake to talk to Big Jim.

"Jim," said Tommy. "I told my father and mother I would learn to swim this year. I don't want to break my word. Is it too late to learn?"

"I'm afraid so," said Big Jim. "There are only two weeks left, and I don't have time to work with you."

"Please, Jim," said Tommy, "I do want to learn. I'll try to make it up to you. I'll help you paint your boat. I'll wash your dog. I'll pick up the paper bags and pop bottles that dirty up the place."

Big Jim grinned. "Why, Tommy," he said. "Suddenly you do want to learn! I hoped you would some day. Maybe it isn't too late."

Big Jim told Tommy to come to the lake the first thing each morning. They would work together with no one watching.

The next morning Tommy splashed into the water beside Big Jim. "Now," said Big Jim. "Duck under the water, head and all."

Tommy ducked down. The water splashed in his nose and ears and eyes. He didn't like it, but he didn't say anything.

Big Jim said, "Now put your face down in the water and make bubbles." He took in a deep breath and showed Tommy what to do. Tommy made bubbles and more bubbles until he didn't feel the water on his face.

Big Jim said, "That's enough. Do you know what you have learned?"

"No," said Tommy. "What?"

"You have learned to breathe out under water," said Big Jim. "You must breathe this way if you are going to swim well."

The next thing Big Jim did surprised Tommy. Big Jim always took small stones out of the lake in places where the water was not deep. Now suddenly he threw two little stones in!

"Tommy," said Big Jim. "See if you can keep your eyes open and find those stones."

Tommy said, "I'll try." He took a deep breath and put his head under the water. He tried to force his eyes open but he couldn't.

Big Jim laughed. "That's all right, Tommy," he said. "We'll try something else. Take a deep breath and put your face into the water. Open your eyes and tell me which of my hands you see. Ready?"

Tommy put his face into the water. This time he forced himself to open his eyes. Then he lifted his head. "I didn't see anything," he said, "but I opened my eyes. It wasn't so bad. Let me try it again."

Tommy tried over and over again. Soon he was able to keep his eyes open.

"Good," said Big Jim. "Our time before the others come is almost up. Would you like to try for those stones again?"

"Yes," Tommy said. He took a deep breath, went under, and forced his eyes to stay open. He found both of those stones and brought them up.

Big Jim put his arm around Tommy. "Good boy!" he said. "That's one of the really hard steps in learning to swim. Now go home and come back tomorrow."

The Surprise

When Tommy got home his mother asked, "Why are your eyes so red, Tommy?"

"I'm just learning something," Tommy answered. He didn't say what he was learning, for he wanted it to be a surprise.

The second morning Big Jim asked Tommy to bring up the two stones again. The first time it was hard for Tommy to force his eyes open. He managed to do it, though. Again and again he went down and brought up the stones.

"Now for the next step," said Big Jim. "You're going to learn to float. Watch how I do it." Tommy watched, and then the lifeguard held Tommy up as he tried. Soon he was floating almost as well as Big Jim.

103

The third morning Big Jim showed Tommy how to move his arms and legs. Then he said, "You have learned many things, Tommy. Now I want you to fit them all together. I'm going to step back and I want you to swim over to me. Take a deep breath, breathe out under the water, then come up for another breath. Keep your face down and make bubbles. Keep your arms and legs moving all the time."

Tommy managed to do all the things he had learned. He splashed through the water until he reached Big Jim. "I can hardly believe it," he cried. "I was swimming! I splashed a lot but I was really swimming!"

Big Jim grinned and said, "You learned even more quickly than I had hoped."

Tommy worked hard. By the end of the two weeks he could swim all the way to the raft. He no longer had to force his eyes to stay open. He didn't splash much, either. "Big Jim," said Tommy, "how can I ever thank you for helping me?"

"I'll tell you how," said Big Jim. "I'm going to ask everyone to come to the lake tomorrow. We're going to have a party. There will be swimming contests for those who have been swimming all summer. You're not ready to go into a contest, but I will ask you to swim to the raft. When I ask you, will you do that for me, Tommy? We won't tell anyone. It will be a big surprise."

Tommy laughed. "I'll do it, Jim. I'll get across to that raft some way."

All the children were at the party with their mothers and fathers. Big Jim blew his whistle and the contests started. Tommy sat beside Big Jim and watched the race. The children were to swim to the raft and back. The first ones to do it would receive prizes.

When the contests were over, Big Jim gave out the prizes. Then he held up his hand until everyone was quiet. "Friends," he said, "I have a surprise for you. Are you ready, Tommy? Go ahead, boy, and show us what you can do."

Tommy raced to the lake. As he ran, someone yelled, "Stop him! He'll get hurt. He can't swim!" Some of the children stood up and stared out at the water. They saw the boy who couldn't swim. He was swimming!

Tommy swam over to the raft. As a surprise for Big Jim, he managed to swim back again, too. He was tired when he came out, but that didn't matter. He saw Big Jim smile. Above the children's shouting he heard his father's voice.

Big Jim blew his whistle. When it was quiet he said, "This has been a good summer at the lake. Many of the boys and girls have learned to swim. It was hard for some and not so hard for others. It was hardest of all for Tommy. Two weeks ago he couldn't swim at all. But he found out that he really wanted to learn. He wanted it enough to work at it very hard. By hard work he has—well, you can see what he has done."

Big Jim held up another prize. "This is a prize of my own," he said. "It is the prize I received in my first swimming contest twenty years ago. I shall give it to the boy who had to work hardest to learn to swim. Tommy, will you come up here, please?"

Tommy was so surprised that he could hardly walk over to Big Jim. Everyone at the party seemed to be laughing and yelling. Tommy saw his father's face. He had a quiet smile. Tommy had kept his word and learned to swim. Tommy's father and mother were as happy as Tommy himself.

The Roundup

Mark wanted to be a cowboy. He wanted to show Mr. Langford that he was learning the work of a cowboy quickly. Mr. Langford was the owner of the ranch where Mark was staying. He might send Mark away if Mark didn't show him he would make a good cowboy. Mark wanted to stay.

Mark liked Shag best of all the cowboys on the ranch. Shag was teaching him the things that mattered to a cowboy.

"Now we're going to round up the cattle," Shag told him. "The cowboys will ride two by two. We will make what is called a circle. We will listen to Old Roan and do as he says."

"Get ready!" Old Roan called to the cowboys.

The cowboys jumped on their horses. Mark got on his horse, too. "I wonder if Old Roan will let me help?" he thought to himself. Then he listened, as Old Roan shouted again.

"Bring the cattle together on that flat!" called Old Roan.

Shag rode close to Mark. "See that flat land over there?" he said. "The land beyond those bushes, I mean. That's where Old Roan wants us to take the cattle."

"String out!" called Old Roan.

Mark knew the meaning of this from watching the cowboys. They rode away two by two to make a circle. He could hardly wait to find out if Old Roan would let him help in the roundup. He wanted to hear this even more than the things Shag was telling him.

Shag said, "At first the circle will be big. Later the boys will close in. They will drive the cattle into a smaller and smaller circle, until they are all on the flat."

There was one thing Mark had been wondering about. "Why do the cattle have to be brought to the flat?" he asked.

Shag said, "Each calf must be found and a brand put on it. Also, Mr. Langford must choose some cattle to sell."

Mark didn't ask what a brand was. He didn't understand all cowboy language, but that didn't matter to him right now. He was thinking about the circle again. "Old Roan may think a city boy can't be of any help," he was thinking. "Well, this city boy can. If he'll let me try, I'll show him what a city boy can do."

Just then Old Roan shouted, "Shag and Mark!"

"Here we are!" cried Mark. Off he rode, with Shag at his side. He felt quite grown up. He was helping to do important work on the ranch.

"We have to go beyond the water holes," said Shag. "That way we will get all the cattle up here. Keep count, Mark. That is one of the hardest things to do. I want to see if you get the right number of cattle that we turn back."

They went by a water hole where cattle were drinking. "Ten!" Mark counted, as they turned the animals back toward camp.

As they rode, Mark and Shag looked everywhere for cattle. They didn't always ride close together. Mark counted ten cattle. Then he counted one group of ninety-five. He thought the next group had twenty-nine, but he wasn't sure. He quickly counted again. Yes, twenty-nine was right. All were turned toward the camp. Mark was careful to count each group. The number must be right.

Suddenly Shag gave a signal to stop. "Here is the fence!" he shouted.

Mark saw a wire fence and knew that Mr. Langford's land ended there.

114

Hi-yi-yiippi-yi

Later when he and Shag came together, the cowboy stopped his horse. "How many cattle did you count between the water holes and the fence?" Shag asked.

Mark was quiet for a second. "What if I didn't manage to count right," he said to himself. At last he said in a low voice, "Two hundred eight."

"Right!" Shag yelled. "You're getting along fine."

"Why, thanks, Shag," Mark said. He wished Mr. Langford had heard him say two hundred eight. He felt even more grown up. A real cowboy had to count cattle right and he had done it.

Mark helped Shag drive the cattle down the sides of the hills. He and Shag had covered their end of the circle. Now all they had to do was to keep the animals moving toward the camp. Just beyond the camp was the flat where they were going.

They came to a shelf of rock and stopped. From there they could watch the roundup. From all sides the circle was growing smaller and smaller. The cattle came walking slowly over hills and flats. The circle had worked. Mr. Langford's cattle were being brought together.

Mark saw that the animals were not hurried. They were just kept moving slowly toward camp.

"Never make cattle run," Shag told him. "If you do they won't weigh as much. If they don't weigh as much we won't receive as much money for them."

"Cowboys have to know so many things," Mark said to himself. "I wonder if I'll ever know them all."

It grew dark as Mark and Shag rode on.
Soon they reached the camp. The dark land
made the top of the wagon look very white.
The smell of food floated out to meet them.

Beyond the bushes the flat looked like a
circus lot filled with animals. In the dark
Mark could almost believe the cattle to be
tigers and bears. Some cattle were lying
down, others were standing. Each calf
seemed to be with its mother.

Far off there were sounds of high voices.
"Hi-yi-yiippi-yi! Hi-yi-yiippi-yi!" cowboys
shouted. "Hi-yi-yiippi-yi!"

118

Mark and Shag rode to the flat. The cowboys rode around and around the cattle, working them into a close group. Cattle kept moving in slowly from all sides. Some of the animals stopped beside the spring to drink. Now and then an animal tried to break away, but the cowboys managed to head it back.

Soon many cattle began lying down. Each calf went to sleep beside its mother. The animals had had enough grass and water. Tired and happy, they soon were lying in one dark group. They didn't need a fence to keep them together.

"Our work is done," said Shag.

Mark and Shag rode quickly back to the camp. They smelled meat cooking and hot corn bread. Some of the cowboys were sitting around the fire waiting for supper.

Mark was hungry, but that didn't matter. Before eating he took care of his horse. He took him beyond the fire to the place where the other horses were. He gave him food and brought him water. Then suddenly he threw his arms around him.

"I counted the cattle right," he whispered to the horse. "I helped with the circle, also. Now Mr. Langford will know that I'll make a good cowboy. Now he's sure to let me stay on the ranch. Hi-yi-yiippi-yi! Hi-yi-yiippi-yi!"

The Work Cowboys Do

Cowboys of long ago helped to make the West a good place to live. Cowboys of today are helping to keep it that way.

The work cowboys do has been about the same through the years. Even in the days of the Old West cowboys worked hard. They had little time for fighting Indians or looking for rustlers. That kind of adventure is for TV cowboys, not real ones.

Some things are different today than they were long ago. In the Old West cowboys had to ride horses to get around the ranch. Today's cowboys sometimes ride in fast pick-up trucks, instead.

The way of selling cattle is not the same today as it was long ago. Then cowboys had to take the cattle to a place where somebody would buy them. They had to drive them a long distance. This was called a "cattle drive."

A cattle drive took many days. The cowboys could go only about ten miles a day. One cowboy would ride faster than the others. This cowboy did not drive cattle. Instead, he rode ahead and found a good place for everybody to stay at night.

Today there are not many cattle drives. Instead, ranchers send their cattle in trucks.

One thing that is not very different from long ago is the rodeo. Cowboys still like to show how well they do their work. The rodeo is the place they can do this.

Everybody has fun watching a rodeo. Bands play. People shout for the cowboys and wave their hats. Many think Rodeo Day is the most important day in the year.

Some cowboys become rodeo stars. They go all across the country every year and ride in many rodeos. People who see them find out that real cowboys can do far more than TV cowboys.

Real cowboys know how to "round up" cattle. That means to drive the cattle to one place. The cowboys do this once a year and it is called a "roundup." They must get the cattle from a ranch together so that each new calf can be branded.

Before branding a calf, a cowboy must first rope it. That means he rides along beside it and catches it with a long rope. Second, he "throws" the calf, which means he makes it fall to the ground. Third, he ties the calf's legs. Then he holds the calf's head down while another cowboy puts on the brand.

A calf is branded with a hot branding iron. The branding iron is put lightly to the calf's side. Cowboys say that the branding iron doesn't hurt the calf. Only a calf knows if this is true.

Branding a calf is like printing the owner's name on it. Anybody who finds a calf can tell who owns it by looking at the brand. Each rancher has a brand that is different from the brands of other ranchers.

Here are some brands with the words
used to say them. You read some brands
the way you read a word, from left to right.
The brand 2-X is called "Two Bar X."

You read this brand, A, from the outside
to the inside. It is called "Circle A," not
"A Circle."

Many brands are made of just one letter.
A letter is made in many different ways.

If a letter is falling over, cowboys use
the word "tumbling." Here is a brand
called the "Tumbling R":

A letter on its side is called "lazy." This is the "Lazy R":

A letter with wings is called "flying." This is the "Flying R":

This is the "Rocking R":

Numbers are used the same way that letters are used. Here are some number brands:

Lazy Two   Tumbling Two   Rocking Six

Now that you know how brands are made, you can make them, also. If you had a ranch, what would you use for your cattle brand?

Way Out West

Way out west where cowboys ride,
Prairie dogs and gophers hide
In burrows with the desert owls
And tremble when the coyote howls.

The prairie stretches to the sky
And miles of grass grow green and high
Where cattle graze, while cowboys guard
The herd, and ride their horses hard.

The prairie stretches wide and far
Beneath the sun, beneath the star.
The cowboy rides his horse for miles,
To watch the herd with songs and smiles.

His partner watches through the night
And sings until the sky grows bright.
Then through the day he rides around
Till every lost calf has been found.

Dorothy Scofield

The Rainiest Day of the Year

Once a year Katie's teacher took his class on a trip to the city. Katie and her friends talked about the trip weeks before it happened. Then at last the day came when they climbed into the school bus and started. No one knew then that this was going to be the rainiest day of the year.

The children sang about the rain. They sang about the way it made the highway shine. They sang about the way it wet the windows. They sang for a long time. At last the bus came to a small country village. The driver called out, "Is anyone hungry? There's a store here that sells good cookies."

129

Adapted with permission of The Macmillan Company and Miriam E. Mason from "Teacher's Helper," from *Katie Kittenheart* by Miriam E. Mason. Copyright 1957 by The Macmillan Company.

"Oh!" cried Katie. "I must go back home!"

Everybody stared at Katie in surprise. "What is it, Katie?" her teacher asked. "Don't you feel well?"

"It's not that," Katie said. "I forgot something important! My kitten, Snoopy, fell into the wash this morning and got all wet. Then he climbed into the oven because it was warm there. Grandmother had just baked a cake. I closed the door so the oven would stay warm. When I left I forgot to open it. Snoopy is still in the oven!"

"Oh, he will jump out when someone opens the door," said a big girl.

"No one is at home," Katie told her. "It is up to me to look after Snoopy. I have got to go home right away!"

Katie's friends were very unhappy that Katie was going to miss the trip. They bought cookies and gave some to her. The teacher was unhappy, also, but he put Katie on a bus going back to her home. He and the others then rode on toward the city.

It was pouring rain when Katie reached her house. Snoopy was sound asleep. He woke up and meowed when Katie opened the oven door. "Just a second, please," Katie told Snoopy. She put on dry clothes, then gave the hungry kitten some warm milk. Then Katie had something to eat, too.

"I haven't a thing to do all afternoon," she told Snoopy. "I know, I will go to school and help Miss Mindy. The children in her class are so little that she can certainly use help."

Katie put on her rain coat and hat and hurried out. She waited until a truck driver who worked on the highway came by. Katie knew the driver well. "Will you drive me to the road where the school is?" she asked.

"Certainly, Katie," said the truck driver. "I would take you right up to the school, but I'm in a hurry. Water is running over the road a few miles away. All highway trucks must be there to help the cars get through. Did you ever see such rain? It's a great day for ducks."

"It may be a great day for me, too," said Katie. "I have always wanted to help Miss Mindy. Today is the first day I have had time to do it. My own class is on a trip."

It didn't take long to reach the school. Miss Mindy was glad to see Katie. "I am thankful you are here," she said. She was bending over a little boy who was stretched out on the floor.

"Jack was jumping on the steps," Miss Mindy told Katie. "He fell and cut his head. I have to drive him to a doctor at once. I cannot leave these little children with no one to take care of them, though. I tried to reach someone on the telephone, but I couldn't. There is a break in the telephone wires because of the storm."

"I am thankful I had to come back home," said Katie. "Now I can take care of the children for you."

"Yes, Katie, that is true," said Miss Mindy. "Even though you are quite little, I believe you can. It is just a short distance to the doctor's, and I will hurry right back. If the school bus comes for the children, send them home." She picked Jack up and hurried off to her car.

Teacher's Helper

Katie looked at the children in the class. They were all quite small, but the noise they made was not small. "If you'll be quiet," said Katie, "I will read a story to you." She picked up a picture book and began to read.

The children did not listen to Katie. A few began running around the room. A boy threw a paper airplane. It hit the girl ahead of him, and she yelled. In the back of the room a fight was starting. In the front someone was making funny faces. This made the rest of the children laugh.

"Sit down, please," cried Katie above the noise. "Be a little more quiet, please!"

A boy in the back called out loudly, "You are not our teacher. You're only a girl."

A girl in the front said, "We don't have to listen to you."

Katie was scared, but she was not going to let the children know it. She had tried shouting louder than the children. That just made them shout louder than ever. Katie thought to herself, "I know what! I will do just as Miss Mindy does."

Katie stood just as tall as she could. She looked at first one of the children, then another. The children began to sit down and be quiet. Then, in a soft voice, Katie said, "I am taking Miss Mindy's place for a short time. You are going to sit down and be quiet until she gets back."

Katie looked and sounded just like a teacher. Soon all the children were in their seats and the room was quiet.

Katie smiled at the children and said, "Now I shall read you a story."

The story was about a jumping calf who frightened away some Indians. Some of the story was very funny and some was frightening. The children liked it and listened quietly. Katie read every word of the book to the children.

Then Katie asked if any one in the class had ever seen a jumping calf. A third grade boy spoke up. He told about a jumping calf on his grandfather's farm. It was a very funny story. The children laughed at the funny things the calf did. The boy felt proud that he had made them laugh.

A little girl knew a poem about a wobbly calf. She was glad to say it for the children. They liked it so much that the little girl felt quite proud.

By this time it was getting late in the afternoon. The children were getting tired.

137

"I wonder when Miss Mindy or the bus driver will come," Katie began to think. The children sang for a while. Then Katie looked at her watch. It was quite late. The room was growing dark. Katie tried to turn on the lights but they wouldn't go on. Then she saw that a few of the children were falling asleep.

"Now let's all go to sleep for a short time," she said. The children put their heads on their arms and rested. A little boy was first to lift his head. "When can I go home?" he wanted to know.

"You'll certainly go home some time," Katie said with a smile. She didn't feel like smiling though. Katie was as tired as the rest of the children. She hoped Miss Mindy or the bus driver would come soon.

Help at Last

Suddenly there was a strange sound that seemed to come from above. Katie put on her rain coat and hat and hurried outside. Rain was still pouring. Water covered the rocky dirt road. An airplane was above the school. As Katie watched, some packages fell from it. On one of the packages was a letter addressed: To the Teacher.

"I am the teacher until Miss Mindy comes back," Katie said to herself. She opened the letter and stood outside the door to read it.

The letter said: "Because of the pouring rain, all roads are under water. Stay in the school until help comes. In the packages are food and bed covers to keep the children warm."

Katie whispered to herself, "I am thankful the school is on a hill." Then she went inside. "That was an airplane," she told the children. "It dropped surprise packages for us."

A number of children helped to bring in the packages of food and bed covers. It was like a picnic. They soon ate all the food.

"Now," Katie said, "we will curl up on the floor under the covers and sleep."

"I don't want to sleep here," said a little boy. "I want to go home. I feel like crying."

"We will all cry," said Katie. "Then we will stop crying and go to sleep."

The children cried for a short time. Then a little girl began to laugh. "Isn't it funny?" she said. "We are going to sleep with our clothes on!" The rest of the children laughed, too. Katie was thankful that they weren't unhappy any more. Soon they were all sound asleep between the bed covers. Then Katie went to sleep, too.

141

In the morning loud noises woke Katie and the children. A number of trucks were parking in front of the school. Miss Mindy was in one of them. Two newspapermen were there taking pictures of the children as they came running out.

All the children wanted to talk about their big adventure. Now that it was over it seemed like fun. "Katie was so brave. She took care of us," they said.

"We are proud of you, Katie," said a newspaperman. "We are going to write a story about you. Would you like us to call it 'Brave School Girl'?"

Katie laughed and said, "We were all scared. We weren't brave. Just call it 'The Rainiest Day and the Strangest Night'!"

A Poem for Babs

David Day had a little sister named Babs. She thought that David could do anything. He liked her to think that, too!

David loved his little sister very much. He was unhappy when she got a cold and had to stay in bed. He wanted to do something to make Babs feel better, but her head hurt and she felt sick. Not a thing he could do pleased her.

"I'll read you a story," David said.

"No! No!" cried Babs in a cross voice. "I don't want a story. Tell me about the bike you are going to win."

"I may not win the bike," said David.

Babs was talking about a newspaper contest. The newspaper was going to give a bike as a prize. The prize would go to the girl or boy who made up the best poem.

David liked to make up poems. He had mailed two of his poems to the newspaper. Babs was sure that he would get the prize. She said so now.

"Yes, you **will** get the bike," she said. "You make the best poems of all. Make one for me now, David. Make up a poem about playing with me."

"Oh, Babs!" said David. "I wish you were big enough to understand things. It takes time to make up a poem. I cannot do it just like that."

"You can, too!" cried Babs. "You've done it before. You just don't want to." She began to cry.

144

David was unhappy. He knew that Babs was cross because she felt so sick. He tried hard to think of a poem, but the words wouldn't come.

"Don't cry, Babs," he said. "Your tears are getting the sheet wet."

Babs looked at the wet sheet, but she kept on crying.

"Your cold can't get better if you cry like that," said David.

Babs didn't answer. She just kept on crying. David became more and more unhappy. He was afraid Babs might become sicker if he didn't think of a poem.

At last David said, "All right, Babs! I'll make a poem for you. Just wait a little while and I'll be back with it."

David hurried to the shelf where he kept his new book of poems. He had thought of a poem in it that was about a game. It was just the kind of poem Babs had asked him to make.

"I'll use it to make her stop crying," thought David. "Then, when she isn't sick and cross I'll tell her that it came from a book."

David read the poem over and over until he could say it to himself. Then he got an old sheet with holes in it and put it over his head. He was peeking out through the holes. His legs were sticking out from under the sheet.

"Here I come!" he called. Then he gave a loud shout and ran into Babs' room.

When Babs saw David in the sheet, she stopped crying in surprise.

David said, "Here's your poem."

My brother is inside the sheet
That gave that awful shout.
I know because those are his feet
So brown and sticking out.

And that's his head that
   waggles there
And his eyes peeking through—
So I can laugh, so I don't care:
"Ha!" I say. "It's you!"

147

Babs laughed out loud. "Ha! It's true, it is you!" she cried. "I see your feet sticking out! I see your eyes peeking through! And your head waggles, too! You didn't frighten me, David. I knew it was you."

"You did?" asked David, making believe he was surprised.

Babs was so pleased with the game and the poem that she forgot how awful she felt. She had David repeat the poem over and over. Soon she could say it, too.

148

The Story Grows

Mrs. Day came in to see about Babs. She was happy to find her looking better.

"David!" cried Babs, "Mother must hear your poem. I'll say it and you play the game."

David didn't know what to say. He wanted to explain to his mother that it was not really his poem, but there was Babs. Would she begin crying again?

"I'll explain to Mother when we get away from Babs," he thought. He put the sheet on and let Babs repeat the poem.

Mrs. Day laughed. "Eyes peeking through. Feet sticking out," she said. "That's you, all right, David. Your head waggles, too!"

149

Babs said, "I am the sister in the poem. David made it up just for me."

Mrs. Day stared at David in surprise. "Why, David!" she said. "That's the best poem you've ever made. It's better than the ones you sent to the newspaper. You should mail that poem to the contest!"

"It's too late," said David, feeling awful. He waggled one foot and stood looking down at it. "The poems had to be mailed in by today," he said.

"That's right," his mother answered. "This is the last day of the contest."

"I wish I could tell her the truth," thought David. "What shall I do? I'll tell her the truth as soon as Babs goes to sleep."

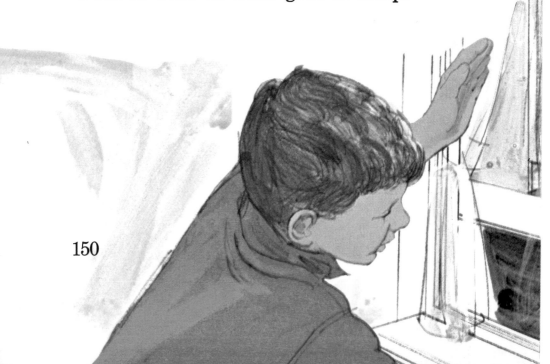

Babs did not take a nap that afternoon. When Mr. Day came home she was still awake. Before he could even take off his coat, Babs asked him to sit down. Then she repeated the poem to him.

"Well!" said their father. "David, of all the poems you've made up this is the best. I'm proud of you."

David couldn't say anything. He just stood there, looking down at his feet as he waggled one of them. "How can I tell him the truth now?" he thought. "This is awful. It's getting harder and harder. Why did I ever let this thing get started? I don't see how I can explain now!"

"I wish David had mailed that poem to the newspaper," said Mrs. Day. "But the contest closes today."

"That doesn't matter. It doesn't have to be mailed," said Mr. Day. "Write the poem, David, and I'll take it right down to the newspaper. I feel sure you'll win the bike."

Win the bike! David wanted that bike more than he had ever wanted anything. Or did he?

"I . . . I . . . I don't remember the poem," he said in a low voice.

"I remember it," spoke up Babs. "Get some paper, David. I'll say the poem to you."

"Yes," said Mr. Day. "Get some paper, David, and write it down. I'll take it to the newspaper right away."

"What shall I do?" thought David. "What shall I do?"

What do you think David did?

153

What Is It?

1. There are three of us in two,
   Five of us in seven,
   Four of us in nine
   And six in eleven.

2. What belongs to you that your friends
   use more than you do?

3. What is it that somebody else has to
   take before you can get it?

Can You Read This?

I had an old saw,
And I bought a new saw.
I took the handle off the old saw
And put it on the new saw,
And of all the saws
I ever saw saw
I never saw a saw saw
Like the new saw sawed.

1. Letters   2. Your name   3. Your picture

154

The Pasture

I'm going out to clean the pasture spring;
I'll only stop to rake the leaves away
(And wait to watch the water clear, I may):
I shan't be gone long.—You come too.

I'm going out to fetch the little calf
That's standing by the mother. It's so young
It totters when she licks it with her tongue.
I shan't be gone long.—You come too.

Robert Frost

155

Can You Believe It?

157

Till's Monkeys and Owls

Once upon a time there was a man named Owlglass—Till Owlglass. He was a man who liked to laugh and make others laugh. Till Owlglass went from city to city. When he went to visit a place, people were glad to see him.

Till knew how to do many things well. It was never hard for him to get work. In one city that he visited, he got work helping a baker.

The baker was an unhappy man. All he did was worry.

Till was a happy man. He would awake with the sun, work hard all day, and not worry at all.

Till liked to mix the dough to make bread and rolls. He sang and laughed as he worked. He beat the dough and sang in time to the beating. When the dough was ready to bake, he danced over to the oven with it. He was never cross.

The baker didn't like to see Till so happy. "What a helper you are!" he said. "I worry about everything, and what do you do? You just laugh and sing!"

The baker was always trying to make Till as unhappy as he was. "Till," he said. "You have spattered dough all over the floor. Wash the floor at once."

Till looked down at the floor. Yes, it was spattered with dough. He knew he was not the one who spattered it, though. He didn't try to explain that the baker had done it.

Now most people would have been cross, but not Till Owlglass. He just laughed. "I'll give that floor a better shine than it has ever had before," he said. Soon the floor was really shining.

Was the baker pleased? He was not. He made Till do all the work the rest of the day.

"Till," said the baker at the end of the day. "It's time for me to stop work. I'm going home. You'll have to stay here and bake."

"Gladly," said Till. "What shall I bake?"

"What shall you bake?" yelled the baker. "You're a baker's helper and you ask what you should bake? What do you think you should do? Bake monkeys and owls?" He pulled his hat down over his ears. Then he stormed out of the shop.

Till stood and laughed until the tears rolled down his face. The baker had given him an idea.

The Idea

What was Till's idea? It was to shape the dough into monkeys and owls! That's just what he did.

He started with the monkeys. He took part of the dough and made father monkeys. They were tall and had very long tails. Then, with another part, he made mother monkeys. They were short and fat. Till also made many monkey children. Some were standing on their heads. Others were hanging by their tails from a branch above them. Still others were jumping through a hoop that was also made of dough.

Then Till made owls in shapes just as funny as the monkeys.

When the baker came the next morning, he stared around in surprise. He saw monkeys and owls everywhere. "Look what you've done!" he cried. "Who ever heard of bread and rolls shaped like this!"

"Why, I just did what you told me to do," said Till. "You said to bake monkeys and owls, so I did."

"You do everything wrong," yelled the baker. "No one will buy such rolls and bread. Pay me for the dough you used."

"If I pay you," said Till, "then these animals will belong to me."

"That's true. Take them and go!" shouted the baker.

Till paid the baker for the dough. Then he took the bread animals and left.

Now Till had another idea! He set up a stand and put his monkeys and owls on it. He stood behind the stand and waited for people to come and buy them.

Till thought everyone would want these funny bread animals. He thought people would be willing to pay more for them. They were harder to make than other rolls.

Till waited for a long time, but no one came to buy. Not a cent did he receive.

"Till Owlglass," he said to himself as he stood behind the stand. "Till Owlglass, you could be wrong, very wrong."

At last a little girl came over to see what Till had on his stand. She took one look at those monkeys and owls and began to laugh.

"Mother!" called the little girl. "Come and see all these funny animals." Her mother joined the little girl.

Soon everywhere Till looked he saw mothers and children. They started at the front of the stand, then circled behind it. They wanted to be sure to see all the animals Till had for sale.

"I choose that fat mother owl," cried a girl. "I choose that monkey with a long tail," cried a boy. And so it went, till every owl and monkey was sold. Till received much more money for the animals than he paid for the dough.

Later the baker heard what had happened. He wanted to be paid more money, but Till had gone. Till was on his way to visit another city.

The Pirate Cook

Oh, once there was a pirate bold
   Who thought that he could cook.
He knew just how to bake a cake—
   He'd read it in a book.

He stirred it up, he stirred it down,
   He stirred it carefully,
He cooked it in the cooking pot,
   And served it up for tea.

The cook was not so pleased with this,
   Until with joy he found
That he could sit upon his cake
   And paddle it around . . .

Marchette Chute

166

The Boy Who Cried Wolf

There was once a boy who took care of sheep near a dark forest. One day he said to himself, "I wish something exciting would happen." Then he thought to himself, "I know what I'll do! I'll make believe a wolf is after the sheep."

In a loud voice he cried out, "Wolf! Wolf!" The villagers ran over to help him. They looked everywhere for the wolf, but there was no wolf.

The next day the boy again wished that something exciting would happen. "Wolf! Wolf!" he cried out louder than before. Again the villagers came running but found no wolf.

167

The third day the boy didn't have to wish for something exciting. A wolf really did come out of the forest and began to chase the sheep.

"Wolf! Wolf!" cried the boy still louder than ever. This time the villagers did not come to help the boy. The wolf killed quite a few sheep and the boy couldn't chase it away.

Later he asked the villagers, "Why didn't you come and save my sheep?"

One villager spoke for the rest. "Boy," he said. "You cried 'wolf!' twice when there was no wolf. How could we know that this time a wolf was really there?"

A Dollar for a Donkey

One day the Mullah, an important man in the village, went to his barn. He planned to get on his donkey and go visit a friend. "What's this?" he cried, when he opened the barn door. The donkey was gone.

The Mullah was very angry with his little donkey. He ran around as fast as he could, looking for her everywhere. His long coat got caught on a berry bush. He was spattered from head to foot with dirt when he stopped. Then he saw that his front gate was open.

The Mullah ran out of his gate. "Where is my donkey?" he shouted to everyone on the street. "Help me search for my donkey."

All the villagers knew that the Mullah would be sad without his small white donkey. They joined in the search at once. They chased through the streets. They knocked on doors and asked if anybody had seen the Mullah's donkey. They ran outside the village walls and looked down the roads. "Search for the donkey that belongs to the Mullah," called his friends. Boys joined the search for the donkey. They even climbed to the tops of the tallest trees to see if she was anywhere in sight.

The Mullah ran about looking until he was too tired to move. He sat down to rest on the ground near his gate. His friend, the baker, sat down beside him to visit. Then the potter came along and joined them. The carpenter and a few other friends joined them later.

The Mullah's wife came out with glasses of hot tea for all. While the Mullah was drinking his tea, he talked about his donkey.

"That no-good lazy donkey!" said the Mullah. "If I ever see her again, I'll sell her for a dollar!" That was the Mullah's way of saying again that his donkey was no good.

Selling a donkey for a dollar was just a joke. "Such an idea!" said the baker. "Only a dollar!" said the potter. The carpenter just went on drinking his tea.

171

Just then the Mullah heard the sound of his donkey's feet on the road behind him. He looked around. There was his donkey. On his back rode the baker's boy.

"Where did you find her?" asked the carpenter. "We couldn't find her anywhere."

"I knew where I would go if I were a donkey," said the baker's boy. "I found her eating grass with the sheep and goats."

The Mullah was as happy as he had been cross a second ago. He hugged his playful little donkey. He hugged the baker's boy who had found her. He hugged the baker, too. "You have such a smart boy!" he cried.

Suddenly somebody pulled at the Mullah's coat. The Mullah looked to one side and saw the potter holding up a dollar. On the other side he saw the carpenter with a dollar.

"I'll buy your donkey," the two men said.

"You must be joking," the Mullah said. "You must be playing a game. Surely you know that I wouldn't think of giving up my donkey. Besides, who would sell a donkey for just one dollar?"

"Don't you remember?" asked the potter. "You said that **you** would, if you ever found it." The rest of the villagers told the Mullah that the potter spoke the truth.

"I was joking!" said the Mullah, with a frightened laugh.

"You didn't sound as if you were joking," said the carpenter. "When you said it you weren't laughing."

The Mullah couldn't break his word. That would be wrong. He certainly didn't want to sell his donkey for a dollar, though. He needed time to think. "Meet me at the donkey fair on Saturday," he said. "I shall sell my donkey to the one who will treat it most kindly."

The Mullah's Plan

Everybody was kind to animals when the Mullah was watching. The cats could walk anywhere along the village walls without worrying about being hit by stones. The dogs were washed until their coats had the finest shine. The donkeys were treated like kings!

Most of the time the Mullah was awake, he was thinking of a plan. He wanted to keep his word and also to keep his donkey. One day as he was drinking his tea, he had an idea. On the night before the donkey fair the Mullah bought a piece of rope. No one had any idea why the Mullah should want a piece of rope.

174

On Saturday every man and boy in the village came to the donkey fair. Each hoped to buy the Mullah's donkey. Each hoped the Mullah would think he would treat it the kindest.

Over their loud talk they heard a sound that was never before heard at a donkey fair. It was a howling kind of meow.

The voice of a cat was not strange in a country where cats step softly along every wall. But this was the voice of a cat who felt out of place and unhappy.

The men looked to see where this awful meow was coming from. A short distance ahead they saw a cat tied with a piece of rope. It was tied—of all things—to the tail of the Mullah's donkey! Beside them stood the Mullah acting quite happy.

"It is true, I'll sell my donkey for a dollar," said the Mullah. "Just one thing, though. My donkey and my cat are very good friends. They must not be parted. That is only kind. Who buys my donkey must buy my cat also."

"How much is your cat?" asked many voices. The men reached into their money bags for another dollar or two.

"Oh, my cat is a very important animal," said the Mullah. "Her father caught a mouse for a king. Her mother caught a mouse for his wife. She is one of the finest of cats. For such a great cat I want one hundred dollars."

The men laughed. They were thankful that the Mullah had found a way to keep his donkey. Everybody knew that the Mullah and his donkey should never be parted.

The Brave Potter

Once upon a time there was a potter. He was riding his donkey one night when a great storm came up. The rain came swirling down in sheets. The only light on that dark night was from the lightning.

The potter was not very brave. He was badly frightened. He went to the house of a friend to get out of the storm. When he got there, he hurried inside. The donkey was left untied and it ran away.

A tiger was caught in the same storm. "This is truly no night for a tiger to be out," he said to himself.

The tiger saw a little old house and hurried toward it. He pressed himself close to the wall to get out of the rain.

Inside the little old house was a little old woman. She was getting wet, too, even though she was inside. The roof above was full of holes, and the rain spattered right through them. Drip, drip, drip went the rain on her bed and her table and chairs.

The little old woman hugged herself to keep warm. She ran from one corner to another. She tried to push each thing out of the way of the rain. It was impossible. The drip, drip, drip was everywhere.

"Oh, my cats and kittens!" cried the little old woman as she chased from corner to corner. "Surely my roof will fall in. This terrible drip, drip, drip scares me so! Why, if a tiger were to walk in, he wouldn't frighten me as much as this terrible drip, drip, drip. Oh, my cats and kittens!"

"What can this terrible drip, drip, drip be?" the tiger whispered to himself. "The old woman acts as if she is even more afraid of it than of a tiger!"

The tiger heard the old woman pushing things from one corner to the other. "What a loud noise," he said to himself. "I suppose that must be the terrible drip, drip, drip."

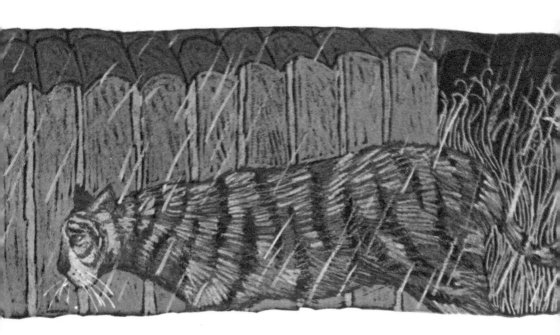

Hold That Tiger!

In the middle of the night the potter came by the little old woman's house. He was searching everywhere for his donkey that had run away. The rain had stopped but it was still very dark. The potter saw the shape of a big animal lying down close to the old house. He couldn't really tell what the shape was in the dark. He supposed it was his donkey. He ran right up to it and took hold of it by the ear. Little did he know that what he was holding was a huge tiger.

"You bad donkey!" he yelled, right into the tiger's ear. "What a trick to pull on me in the middle of the night! Why did you run away? Why did you make me come out and search for you?" He swung at the tiger with all his might. "Get up! Get up!" he cried. "Get up or I'll hit you into the middle of next week."

The tiger blinked in surprise. In all his years nothing had ever frightened him so. "I suppose this must be the terrible drip, drip, drip," he cried to himself. "It makes such noise, and truly it hits so hard!" The tiger got up in a hurry! Of that you may be sure.

The potter leaped on the tiger's back. He still thought the tiger was his donkey.

The tiger whirled around and ran through the woods as fast as he could. In all his years nobody had ever tried to ride him.

"Truly," he thought as he ran. "Nothing on earth is as awful as the terrible drip, drip, drip. No wonder the old woman said she was more afraid of it than of a tiger."

Soon the potter reached home. He tied the tiger to his donkey post with a piece of rope. Then he went to bed.

At sunrise the next morning the potter's wife arose. She looked out the window and blinked her eyes. A great big tiger was tied to the donkey post!

"Man of the house! Are you awake?" she cried to the potter, who was still in bed. "Do you know what animal you rode home last night?"

"Certainly," said the potter. "I rode that no-good donkey of ours."

"Come and see," said his wife. She pointed out the window.

The potter got up and looked outside.
There at the donkey post was the great big
tiger.

The potter blinked in surprise. He
started to feel himself all over to see if the
tiger had hurt him. But no! There he was,
safe and sound. There was the tiger at the
post. That was where he had tied him in the
middle of the night.

"Man of the house," said his wife. "What
say you now?"

"Well," said the potter, waggling his
head. "You might as well know now that
you are living with a very brave man. What
will a brave man do when his donkey isn't
around? Why, he'll ride a tiger—what else?"

Nothing-At-All

Once upon a time there were three little dogs who were brothers. They lived in a far forgotten corner of an old forgotten farm. They lived in three forgotten kennels which stood there in a row.

One of the kennels had a pointed roof. In it lived Pointy, the dog with pointed ears.

Another kennel had a curly roof. In it lived Curly, the dog with curly ears.

The middle kennel had a roundish roof. In it lived the third dog. If he had round ears nobody knew it, for he was a dog no one could see. He was invisible.

He was not very tall
And not very small.
He looked like nothing,
Like nothing at all.
And that was his name—
Nothing-at-all.

Nothing-at-all was happy enough. Though nobody could see him, he acted like any other dog. He had just as much fun. He could jump and run and eat. He could hear and see and smell. He could bark and play and rest with his two little puppy brothers.

Pointy said to Nothing-at-all, "We love you even if we can't see you."

Curly said, "We know you are a really truly dog even if we can't see you. We can't see the wind either but the wind is real. We can't see smells but they are **very** real."

Nothing-at-all said, "Oh, I suppose it takes all kinds of dogs to make a world. It takes both see-able and unsee-able ones. So why should I worry?" He was as happy as any dog could be until one day something happened.

187

It was a warm and lazy day. Pointy was lying in his pointed kennel. Curly was lying in his curly kennel. All three of them were sleeping when the sound of voices woke them.

"Oh, look!" cried a boy's voice. "Here are some dog kennels in this far forgotten corner of the old forgotten farm."

"With dogs in them?" asked a girl's voice.

The boy looked into one kennel and said, "Yes! There's a curly-eared dog in here."

Next he looked into another kennel and said, "There's a pointy-eared dog in here!"

Then he looked into the middle kennel. Now because Nothing-at-all was invisible the boy didn't see him. "The roundish kennel has nothing in it at all," he said.

Ever so carefully the girl reached for Pointy. Ever so carefully the boy reached for Curly. The two little dogs were frightened and began to cry.

"Don't cry, little pointy-eared dog," said the girl. "We won't hurt you. We'll take care of you."

The boy said, "Don't cry, little curly-eared dog. We'll be kind to you. We'll give you milk to drink and bones to nibble."

When Pointy and Curly heard this, they knew they would be safe and happy. They curled up in the children's arms and went back to sleep.

189

Left Behind

Pointy and Curly were taken away to a happy home. Poor Nothing-at-all was left behind. Do you think he sat down and cried? Oh no—he had a plan!

"I'll just be very quiet and go with them," he thought. "After a while they'll get used to me. They'll find out I'm a really truly dog even though they can't see me. Then they'll take care of me, too. They'll give me milk to drink and bones to nibble. I think I will like it very much!"

Those were his thoughts as he chased after the boy and girl and his brothers.

190

It was a long long road, though. Soon his little invisible legs felt tired. His big invisible eyes felt blinky. He had to sit down and rest. His eyes blinked once and twice and three times. Then he was fast asleep. When he awoke he was all alone.

"Oh, where in the world is everybody?" he cried. "I must run and find them!" He ran to the little lake. No one was there. He ran around the berry bushes. No one was there. He ran by the poppy patch. No one was there. In and out he went, over and under, in turns and circles that made him dizzy.

191

At last he found a tree with a big empty
hole in it. It looked something like a kennel.
He curled up inside it. He felt so awful and
so much like nothing. He whispered sadly to
himself:

"Oh, I'm not very tall
And not very small.
I look like nothing,
Like nothing at all!"

As he finished, a voice above him said, "I
can't see you. Are you that empty space in
the tree?" It was a bird who spoke.

"Yes," said the little dog. "My name is Nothing-at-all, and that's what I look like, too. I never cared about being unsee-able before, but now I do. I want to look like other dogs so the boy and girl can see me. They'll give me milk to drink and bones to nibble. They'll take me for their pet as they did my two brothers."

The bird laughed. "That's a long story for an empty space to tell!" he said. "I can understand how you feel, though. I might be able to help you."

"You're only a bird," said Nothing-at-all. "How can you help me?"

"I am a jackdaw," said the bird proudly. "It is my work to bring home everything I see. Once I found a Book of Magic. Wait! I'll be right back," and the bird was gone.

When he came back the jackdaw said, "It's just as I thought. In the Book of Magic there is a page called 'Nothingness and Somethingness.' If someone is Nothing but wants to be Something, it tells him what to do. He must get up at sunrise and whirl around and around and around. While whirling he must say this magic poem:

I'm busy

Getting dizzy.

The book says that he must do this nine days in a row at sunrise. Then he shall see what he shall see. Goodby, I'm off!" and the bird was gone.

194

Something After All

The next morning at sunrise Nothing-at-all awoke and tried the magic. He began whirling and twirling and swirling. He said:

"I'm busy
Getting dizzy."

What do you suppose had happened while he was whirling? Do you think he was now a dog that anybody could see? No, he wasn't. He still looked like Nothing, but now his Nothingness had a shape! He held up his paw. He couldn't see the paw but he could see a paw-shaped space.

"Well done!" cried the jackdaw's voice. "You are a fine looking shape, I must say. Keep it up!" and the bird was gone.

The next day Nothing-at-all worked at his magic. As soon as the sun peeked over the top of the hill he awoke. He whirled and twirled and swirled, and repeated:

"I'm busy
Getting dizzy.
I'm busy
Getting dizzy."

The jackdaw came by and said, "Yes, the magic is working well. That's a fine black spot you have on your back now, one of the finest. Keep it up!" and the bird was gone.

The third day Nothing-at-all whirled and twirled and swirled. He repeated:

"I'm busy
Getting dizzy.
I'm busy
Getting dizzy.
I'm busy
Getting dizzy."

When he sat down to rest, the jackdaw came. He said, "You're doing better than I hoped. You've quite a few more spots today. Goodby!" and he was gone.

The fourth day the jackdaw said, "You are certainly working hard at your magic. That black tail tip is a honey, I must say!"

The little dog was so pleased that he wagged his tail madly. Though the **tail** was still invisible, its black tip showed the wagging. The jackdaw laughed at this. Then he flew off.

By the fifth day, Nothing-at-all's eyes were visible.

By the next day, his nose and mouth could be seen.

On the next day, his back was visible.

On the day after that, his ears and paws could be seen.

197

Then came the last day. Nothing-at-all whirled and twirled and swirled as he had never done before. He was so dizzy that all the world seemed to swirl around with him. When he stopped to rest, the jackdaw came.

"Good work!" cried the jackdaw. "Now you are SOMETHING after all—a really truly see-able dog! And a very dear little round-eared puppy you are, to be sure. I hope you'll be safe and happy! Goodby!"

Now the little dog was so happy that he leaped to his feet. He barked and picked up sticks and danced about madly. Round and round in a circle he ran. With jumps and bounces and turns he ran. In and out, over and under, around little lakes and poppy patches he ran. Then he stopped.

There in front of him were the boy and
the girl. They were coming from the far
forgotten corner of the old forgotten farm.
They were pulling a long red wagon. On it
were the pointed kennel, the curly kennel,
and the roundish kennel!

With a run and a jump, the round-eared
puppy popped into his roundish kennel. Now
he too was taken to a new and happy home.
All along the way he wagged his tail with
the black tip. With happy barks he said:

"I've always been small
And not very tall.
I used to look like nothing at all.
I'm still quite small
And not a bit tall,
But now I'm a see-able dog after all!"

199

The boy and the girl didn't know what the little dog was saying. They didn't know what Pointy and Curly were saying either.

Maybe, almost surely, Pointy and Curly said, "How happy we'll be, all three of us! We have our dear old kennels to live in. We have two kind children to play with. And oh, little Something-after-all, it **is** so good to SEE you!"

The Lion and the Mouse

One day a little mouse forgot to look where he was going. Because of this he ran over the paw of a sleeping lion.

The lion awoke. "What do you mean by this?" he roared. He put his paw over the mouse and opened his mouth to eat him.

"Oh, King of the Forest," cried the frightened little mouse. "Please forgive me and let me go. If you do I'll always remember it. Who knows, great King? One of these days I may be able to do you a good turn."

"What?" roared the lion. "A little mouse like you help me?" He laughed at such an impossible idea. Then he lifted his paw and let the little mouse go.

201

A short time later the lion was caught in a trap. His roars could be heard by all the animals in the forest. The little mouse was awake and heard them, too.

"That is the lion who let me go," he said to himself. "I've got to help him." Off through the forest he ran. He didn't stop for a second until he reached the roaring lion.

The lion was caught in a trap made of rope. The little mouse began to nibble. He nibbled through the rope and made a hole in the trap. The hole was large enough for the lion to step through.

The lion was very thankful. He turned to the mouse and said, "Now I've learned something. I will remember it always. *Little friends may be great friends.*"

Jonathan Bing

Poor old Jonathan Bing
Went out in his carriage to visit the King,
But everyone pointed and said, "Look at that!
Jonathan Bing has forgotten his hat!"
(He'd forgotten his hat!)
Poor old Jonathan Bing
Went home and put on a new hat for the King,
But up by the palace a soldier said, "Hi!
You can't see the King; you've forgotten
   your tie!"
(He'd forgotten his tie!)
Poor old Jonathan Bing,

He put on a *beautiful* tie for the King,
But when he arrived an Archbishop said, "Ho!
You can't come to court in pajamas,
   you know!"
Poor old Jonathan Bing
Went home and addressed a short note to the
   King: If you please will excuse me
         I won't come to tea;
         For home's the best place for
         All people like me!

Beatrice Curtis Brown

203

The World Around Us

Roger and the Fox

"It's a beautiful fall day," Roger thought, as he walked home from school. He listened to the rustle-rustle-crack of the leaves under his feet.

At the bend in the road he heard a different kind of rustle. It was the sound of a wild animal deep in the leaves. Roger started toward the sound. Then he stopped. He stood still as a fence post and waited.

Soon there was another rustle in the leaves and out came a skunk. It ran across the road and was gone.

It was Seth who had told Roger how to act if he wanted to see wild animals. Seth was the man who helped Roger's father with the work on the farm. He seemed to know everything. "Don't go toward wild animals in the woods," he told Roger. "Instead, wait until they come out."

Roger hurried home. He found Seth in the barn milking a cow. "I saw a skunk," he cried. "I just stood still and I saw it run across the road."

Seth went right on with his milking. "I saw a big fox this morning," he said at last. "I didn't know there were any foxes in these woods. There is one, though. A fine red one down at the river. It was near the ironwood tree that was knocked down in the storm."

Suddenly Roger felt as empty as a balloon with no air in it. How important was a little old skunk when Seth had seen a fine red fox? Roger had moved to the country from the city. He had often seen wild animals here in the country. Never a fox, though.

Roger left the barn and hurried down the long hill that led to the river. He hoped to see the fox. It was nearly dark by the time Roger reached the ironwood tree. It was cold, and Roger was hungry. He searched everywhere, but didn't see the fox.

"I'll come back soon," Roger said to himself. "I'll bring Scamper with me." Scamper was Roger's dog. Roger supposed he was almost as smart as Seth's dog. He was sure that Scamper would help him.

A few weeks passed before Roger took Scamper down the long hill to look for the fox. The river looked colder than ever. Scamper ran ahead to keep warm. He was at the ironwood tree when Roger caught up with him. He was barking loudly and smelling the ground.

"Don't be so noisy, Scamper!" Roger said. "That's no way to act. Seth's dog would know better." Then Roger saw the hole! It was a large, roundish hole and it was hardly visible. The ironwood tree hid it. "That must be the fox's front door," he whispered.

He couldn't see the fox anywhere. The fox had heard Scamper's noisy barks and Roger's shouts. He didn't so much as stick his nose out.

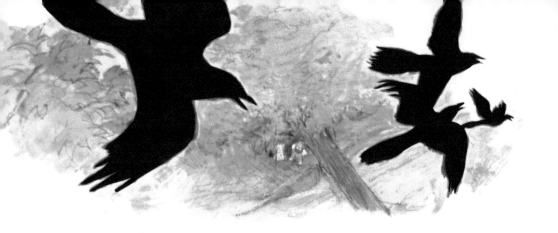

The Fox Who Wasn't There

After that Roger didn't want to visit the fox with noisy Scamper along. He waited for a chance to go alone. It came when his big brother Dick began to train Scamper to do tricks.

This time Roger moved quietly. He didn't even make the leaves rustle. He didn't see the crows on the branches above him. The crows saw Roger, though. Suddenly they began to caw, caw, caw. They lifted their black wings and flew off. The sudden noise made Roger jump. The fox must have jumped, too! He must have jumped right down into his deep hole. When Roger reached the hole the fox was nowhere in sight.

210

On the next Saturday Roger awoke early in the morning. He started for the river.

"Have you had a chance to see the fox yet?" Seth asked as he passed by. Roger said, "No." He couldn't explain to Seth, but he had a feeling this would be an exciting day.

Roger walked very softly until he was near the ironwood tree. Then he hid behind a berry bush and peeked out at the fox hole. What he saw made him blink. He could see the shape of something, but he couldn't tell just what. It was large and reddish-brown. Was it—surely it must be—the fox?

Roger never had a chance to make sure. Just at that second a big hunting dog leaped through the bushes. Behind him were three duck hunters. Roger moved toward them and gave them a signal to be quiet. It was no use. His leg got caught between two branches. He went tumbling down in front of the hunters.

"Well, boy," said the tallest hunter, as he pulled Roger to his feet. "What are you doing out so early?"

"Fox!" whispered Roger, pointing at the hole. The three hunters looked but they didn't see a fox anywhere. "I saw it!" Roger began. "Anyway, I think ___"

"Sure, boy," said the tallest hunter, grinning. "Don't worry. When I was little I used to see lions and tigers in these woods."

Roger knew the tall hunter was teasing him, so he started for home. He felt awful as he climbed up the long hill. He didn't mind falling. He didn't mind the hunter's teasing. What he did mind was that he couldn't be sure he had truly seen the fox. Seth would laugh if he told that to him. Roger would mind that most of all.

After that Roger caught a cold and had to stay in bed. When he was better, the weather kept him indoors. Weeks passed.

Roger hurried straight down to the river as soon as he could go outdoors. The bank of the river was covered with a sheet of ice. It was just made to be jumped on. Roger took his first leap, and the ice cracked. He took another leap and listened to the cracking sound. It was a fine winter noise.

Roger jumped almost all the distance to the fallen tree. It was great fun, but it wasn't the way to see a fox. The fox must have heard all that cracking a long way off. By the time Roger reached the fox's hole, no fox was there.

Roger felt very tired as he climbed up the long hill and walked home. As he passed by the barn, Seth came out. "See the fox?" Seth asked.

"No!" Roger said. "I've always just missed him. Always!" At this point Roger felt it was impossible to see the fox.

Seth grinned, but his voice was friendly enough. "You'll have to be real quiet to see a fox," he said. "Quiet and mighty quick. It wouldn't be easy for a city boy, and that's the truth."

Roger didn't like to be called a city boy. He knew Seth wasn't teasing, so he walked away without saying a word. "Some day," he said to himself, "I'm going to see that fox. I've just got to see it, and I will."

214

Paw Prints in the Snow

The next day was Roger's birthday. Birthdays were always exciting in Roger's family. His mother and dad gave him skis. His brother Dick gave him a duck whistle. Seth gave him the finest thing of all, a hunting hat.

Roger found that it was not easy to learn how to ski. Almost three weeks passed before he could ski down little hills and across the fields. He often went tumbling into the snow. It was very deep snow, too.

Roger was glad he had his skis to keep him busy. Nobody, not even Seth, could have walked far through that deep snow.

At last the day came when Roger could ski down the long hill that led to the river. After that Roger often skied down the long hill. It was not easy to get back up to the top, but Roger didn't mind.

Every day Roger's mother would ring the large cowbell when it was time for dinner. When Roger heard the cowbell ring he left the long hill and headed across the field for home. One day he was just skiing down the last little hill to the front door. His mother came out to ring the cowbell again. She had just picked up the bell when Roger stopped beside her. She was so surprised she jumped and dropped the cowbell in the snow.

"Why, Roger!" she said. "You did surprise me. I didn't hear you coming at all!"

Then Roger had a wonderful idea. If he'd surprised his mother he could surprise the fox! At last he'd found a very quiet, fast way to go places. The deep snow couldn't stop him, either. Tomorrow he'd ski right down to the river and trick that fox!

It snowed all night. Early the next morning Roger climbed to the top of the long hill. A brand new, wonderful world lay before him. Every field and hill was white and shiny and quiet. Roger hugged himself. He was so glad to be the first one out in this brand new world. Then he pushed off and skied down the long hill. He wasn't noisy this time. He stopped near the ironwood tree. He stood as still as a snowman and stared at the fox's hole.

There, straight ahead of Roger's nose, was the fox!

The fox's head was up. His tail was out. He was standing as still as Roger himself!

Suddenly the fox threw back his head and barked. It didn't sound like Scamper. It sounded like nothing on earth but a big, red fox. It was a wild, strange sound. Roger had never heard anything like it in his life.

218

Only Roger's eyes moved as he saw a second fox leap out of the hole! She was smaller and a lighter reddish-brown than the first fox. It was all so exciting that Roger lost his footing. He took a step to keep from falling. The tip of one ski hit a small branch. There wasn't much noise. Just the soft sound of snow falling onto snow on the ground. It was hardly a noise at all, but it was enough!

The two foxes were gone! One second they were right there in front of Roger and the next they were hidden. It was as if they had suddenly become invisible. Roger stared at the place where they had been. Then he grinned from ear to ear. Seth wouldn't be teasing him now.

There were new tracks in the snow where the foxes had stood. Roger looked at the tracks and looked again. The tracks were paw prints, and they were right where he'd seen the foxes!

After that Roger didn't wait another second. He started straight home to tell Seth. This time he hadn't been wrong. He had truly seen the fox. There were tracks to show it. More than that, he'd seen two foxes. That was just twice as many as Seth himself had seen!

220

Miss Abby of the Green Thumb

Alice liked to go places with her mother. She liked the drive down the river road to get eggs most of all. Alice's mother bought all the eggs for her family from Miss Abby. Alice's father never could understand why Alice and her mother went so far to get eggs. Alice and her mother knew why.

Miss Abby lived in a very old house overlooking the river. Everything about the house had come from the land. The stones for the cellar were found in the fields. The wood had been cut from the trees that grew on the land. The bricks had been made from the earth near the river.

Miss Abby had always lived in the old brick house. She had never been many miles away from it. She was happy and busy there. In summer she had her flowers and her yard to keep her busy. In winter she cared for her house plants. She always had flowers around her. There were always cats underfoot and kittens playing around the kitchen.

Miss Abby never missed hearing Alice and her mother drive up. The door would open and there would stand Miss Abby, waving to them.

"Come right in," she would say. "Let's go into the front room." But Alice's mother always asked to sit in the kitchen.

The kitchen was bright with sunshine. Blue and white star flowers were pouring from their hanging baskets in the windows. The window sills were filled with flowering plants.

Miss Abby had a green thumb. She could make anything grow. She often had little packages of seeds to put into the egg basket as a surprise. She grew cuttings from her plants for her friends.

Miss Abby had always been happy until the third morning after the big blizzard. It had been a mild winter, quite warm most of the time. It had been so mild that Alice felt that it was hardly winter at all. Then, just as everyone thought that winter was over, along came the blizzard.

In the middle of the night the temperature dropped down, down, down. The wind roared across the fields. Soon the ground was covered deep with snow.

The blizzard went on for twenty-four hours. There were no cars on the road. All the highway men worked night and day to keep the highways clear. But it was three days before the river road was cleared.

Alice's mother had tried to call Miss Abby on the telephone, but the wires were down. Alice knew her mother was worrying.

On the third day Alice ran home from school. "Mother, Mother!" she called. "The river road is cleared."

In no time at all, Alice and her mother were driving down the river road.

After the Blizzard

Only the middle of the road had been cleared. The snow was as high as the car on both sides. Alice and her mother were glad to get to the old house. They were glad to see that a walk had been cleared across the yard. Everything looked all right, but something was different.

For the first time, there was no sign of Miss Abby. They had to knock at the door. When Miss Abby opened the door, she was not smiling in her old way.

"Come in," she said. "You shouldn't have come way out here just for me."

Alice ran into the kitchen. "Why, Miss Abby!" she said. Miss Abby began to cry.

There was not a flower in the room. The pretty blue and white star flowers were hanging black and ugly from their baskets. All Miss Abby's plants were gone from the window sills.

"I let all this happen," said Miss Abby. "It had been so mild. That night before the blizzard—I had no idea. I let the fire go almost out. Now all my plants and flowers are gone. You know they were all my mother's plants, and her mother's before her. That's why I feel so sad."

Alice's mother did everything she could to make Miss Abby feel better. But Alice and her mother went away feeling very unhappy.

When they got back into their own house Alice ran to the plant table.

"Didn't Miss Abby give you this one, and this, and this, too?" she asked. "And think of all the cuttings she has given to her neighbors! Do you think—"

"Alice," cried her mother. "What good ideas you have." Before she stopped to take off her coat, she hurried to the telephone.

All Saturday afternoon neighbors called at Alice's house. "Let me bring this to Miss Abby. It was a cutting from one of her mother's favorites," said one woman.

Another said, "Here is one of Miss Abby's favorites. Most of my flowers came from her seeds and cuttings." So it went.

The next day was beautiful, and mild. That morning a long row of cars stopped at Miss Abby's house. Friends and neighbors with packages and baskets got out of the cars. The yard was filled with people. Alice ran ahead because it was her idea.

Miss Abby, her eyes bright with surprise, opened the door. Everyone, smiling and talking at once, came pouring in. It was so exciting it seemed like a party.

When Alice opened her package, there was a beautiful white star plant. Alice said, "It's one of yours, Miss Abby."

Miss Abby cried for joy when everyone began handing her plants.

"You gave it to me five years ago—"

"I grew this from your seeds—"

Soon the window sills were full. The plant stand was full. Blue and white star flowers poured down from the baskets. Miss Abby would need her green thumb again.

Her friends had put cakes and other good things on the table. It was a real party.

At last it was time to go.

"Now my flowers will be dearer to me than ever," said Miss Abby. "Thank you all, friends and neighbors."

Joe, the Friendly Snake

Many hundreds of snakes have lived in the zoo where Joe lived. Only one of them was ever a real pet. The name of that pet snake was Joe.

When Joe came to the zoo he was only ten feet long. He wasn't a baby any more, but he wasn't grown up either. He was an anaconda. They are large snakes. Joe would get three times as long before he stopped growing.

Some anacondas just want to be let alone, but Joe was different. He liked to meet people and he liked to be near them. Above all, he liked to explore things.

When Joe came to the zoo he was packed in a box with wire all around it. On the box was a sign saying, "Handle with Care." Inside the box was a sack tied with a piece of rope. Inside the sack was Joe, all coiled up and looking sleepy.

When the sack was untied Joe came out slowly. He slid across the room and looked under a table. When he didn't find anything to eat, he turned around and explored somewhere else. Joe's keeper was watching all the time.

Anacondas have teeth but they don't bite. They squeeze instead. When they catch something to eat, they coil around it and squeeze it. Then they eat it. They don't squeeze people, so the keeper was not afraid.

After Joe had explored every corner of the room, the keeper picked him up. Joe coiled himself around the keeper so he wouldn't fall. Then the keeper brought him to his new home.

It was a fine place to live. There was more than enough room, even for a snake ten feet long. There was a little swimming pool and a shelf of rock where he could coil up and sleep. There was just about everything a snake could want.

Joe lived in that cage for many years. Every morning at nine the keeper came to clean Joe's cage. Joe didn't have a watch, but he knew when it was almost nine. A little before nine he crawled to the back of the cage. He waited there for his friend.

The keeper was supposed to clean Joe's swimming pool. That was not easy when Joe was in the pool. The keeper always tried to make Joe crawl up onto the shelf of rock.

Joe had a better idea. He went right out of the cage when he had a chance. When the keeper picked him up he slid down the keeper's back. He slid right into the hall behind the cages. That was all right, because there were doors at both ends of the hall. Joe couldn't get out and frighten people.

232

While the keeper was busy cleaning, Joe explored the hall. He looked under everything in it. He hoped to find a mouse or something else to eat. He never did find a mouse, but he kept on looking for one. Just because you don't find a mouse today is no sign you won't find one tomorrow. Joe was the sort of snake that always hoped for the best.

Joe explored every dark corner of the hall. When he reached the end he turned around. Now it was visiting time. Joe visited the other keepers in their rooms, which opened into the hall. He didn't trouble them or stop them from their work. He just crawled into each room and explored it. Then he crawled out again.

233

The last thing Joe did was the thing he liked most. He always stopped at the window behind his cage and looked out. He could have stayed there for hours. He could see all sorts of things. He saw people walking around. He saw a big red truck drive up with food for the other animals. Sometimes he saw a big beautiful bird in the yard across the road.

It was all very exciting. Joe never wanted to leave the window when the keeper came for him. Just the same, he coiled himself around the keeper and returned to his cage. He knew that tomorrow he would get to visit his neighbors again. Who knows? Maybe tomorrow would be the day he would discover a mouse!

Granny Saves a Duckling

"I'll take care of the ducks, Faddy," said Granny.

"All right," her husband answered. "That will be fine. I must take these men home. They have worked very hard on the farm today."

Faddy and the men rode off in his car. When her husband had gone, Granny went to feed the ducks. She had no idea what an exciting thing was going to happen.

While the ducks were eating, Granny discovered that one group was missing. It was a mother duck with ten ducklings. Granny searched all over the yard, but there wasn't a sign of the duck family.

Even if they got out of the yard, they should have returned by now. Mother ducks bring their little ones back for supper and a safe place to sleep. The missing family didn't come to the feeding dishes or to the water for baths.

Soon the other mother ducks were asleep. They were under their favorite bushes and in their favorite corners. Their ducklings were under them or around them. The mother and her ten ducklings were still missing.

236

It had been a very hot day. Granny's first thought was the pond. If the mother duck did get out of the yard, that's where she would have gone!

Granny walked in the direction of the pond. Before she even reached it, she heard noisy quacks coming from that direction. They were the sort of quacks that ducks give when they are angry or frightened.

Granny began to run. When she got near the pond, she saw the missing family. The mother was quacking and beating her wings wildly at something under the water. Granny could see that one of the ducklings kept going down. Something seemed to be pulling it under the water. As Granny watched, she discovered that the something was a great huge turtle!

The helpless duckling tried hard to break away from the turtle, but it couldn't. The mother duck tried bravely to save her baby.

As Granny watched she became very angry at that turtle. Without stopping to think, she hurried right into the pond!

Granny had been to town that day. She had on her favorite dress. Still, into the pond she went to save the helpless duckling. She could hardly keep her footing on the bottom of the pond. It was covered with mud. She carefully slid over to where the ducks were.

Granny got a tight hold on that turtle. Then she lifted him right out of the water. He was so surprised that he let go of the duckling. The mother duck quickly called her little ones. She swam out of the pond and they followed behind her. She led them up the hill in the direction of the yard.

Granny blinked when she saw how awfully big and heavy the turtle was. She stared at his mean-looking head and mouth. Then she tried to throw him onto the bank. He was so big and heavy and coated with mud that Granny lost her footing. The turtle slid back into the water. Granny went tumbling to the bottom of the pond! The turtle was gone when she crawled slowly to her feet again.

The Missing Duckling

Granny climbed out of the mud and water and up the bank. She caught up to Mrs. Duck and counted the ducklings. Only nine! Where was the one Granny had saved?

Granny returned to the pond. She hunted everywhere for the duckling, but there was no sign of him.

"Was I too late?" she asked herself. "Did that helpless little duckling sink to the bottom and get drowned?"

Granny suddenly had an idea. "The duckling may be hurt," she said. "He may have hidden somewhere. His mother didn't wait for him because I was here. Instead, she got the rest of her family away safely."

Granny stood at the pond. Drip, drip, drip went the water off her hair. Granny had plenty of reddish-brown mud spattered all over her. It began to cake on her dress and legs and felt awfully heavy.

There were some blueberries on a bush near her. As Granny waited and listened, she picked a berry. When she pulled at the bush, she heard a rustle under the leaves. Then she heard a helpless little peep. She leaned down and looked under the bush. Sure enough, there was the duckling. He was still wet and frightened. As he tried to move, Granny saw that he was lame. That's why he hadn't followed his mother. Granny would have to carry him.

Granny picked the duckling up and tried to warm him and dry him. She held him close as she walked in the direction of the yard. The rest of the duck family was almost home.

When Granny got near enough, she showed the duckling to the mother duck. They followed along, with Granny still carrying the duckling. The mother duck watched her closely. When the ducks were safely in the yard, having a late supper, Granny left them.

Granny looked a sight as she went toward the house. Her husband, who had returned, stared at her in surprise. "What has happened to you? Are you hurt?" he cried.

Granny grinned. "No, don't worry," she told Faddy. "I was down at the pond. At it and in it! I am spattered with plenty of mud. I must go up the back way and take a bath."

Later Granny had a cup of hot tea. She told her husband what had happened. Faddy began teasing Granny at the idea of her hurrying into the pond in her favorite dress.

"I'm still plenty mad," said Granny. "To think that I let that turtle get away!"

"It's not so funny," said her husband. "The truth is you were quite thoughtless. One bite and that turtle could have taken your thumb off. We have to get rid of him, or he'll always be after the ducks."

Early the next morning Faddy and the men emptied the pond. When the water was out, they discovered two huge heavy turtles at the bottom.

"Let's take them to the river," said Faddy. "They'll be too far from the farm to get a chance to trouble us there."

Granny leaned over and looked down at the turtles. "I really was thoughtless," she said. "If I had stopped to think, I never would have gone after that big heavy turtle. I'm thankful I did, though, for he could have given us plenty of trouble."

As for the duckling, his lame foot was well in two days. His mother never left the yard again until the ducklings were grown. By that time the pond was full and the ducklings were no longer helpless.

244

A Hummingbird Gets Out

Zoo keepers try very hard to make sure that no animal escapes. They are most careful with the birds. If a four-footed animal escapes, its tracks can be seen on the ground. The keeper can follow the tracks. Maybe he can even run faster than the missing animal. Then it is easy for him to catch it.

When a bird escapes, it may fly to the top of the tallest tree. Often it's impossible to catch it. That's why the people who work in the Bird House are so very careful. They try never to let a bird escape from its cage.

Sometimes it happens, though. It happened one morning while the keeper was giving the hummingbirds their breakfast.

Early every morning the keeper goes to the Bird House to fix the hummingbirds' breakfast. A little bottle hangs on the wall of each cage. The bottle is filled a few times a day with a sweet drink that hummingbirds like. The hummingbirds flutter their wings very fast and hang in the air in front of the bottles. Hummingbirds have long tongues. They dip their tongues into the sweet drink and lick it up.

Each morning the keeper has to take the bottles out of the cages. He has to carry them to the sink to empty them. Then he has to wash them and fill them again. He tries to be very careful to close and lock the cage doors. One morning he was thoughtless. He forgot to lock one door.

There was no trouble at first because the cage door stayed shut. The keeper took the bottle and washed it in the sink. He placed it on the drainboard with all the other bottles. Then he went to another corner of the room to fix the hummingbirds' breakfast. Just at that second the door of the cage swung wide open. A hummingbird flew out.

The keeper turned and saw the bird fluttering over the empty bottles on the drainboard. The door to the outside was wide open. The hummingbird could escape!

For a short time the keeper stood there, feeling helpless. "Oh!" he thought. "That's one of the best hummingbirds in the zoo. If I move, it will fly out. What shall I do?"

The hummingbird kept sticking its long tongue into the spouts of the empty bottles. More than once it flew toward the wide open door. Instead of flying out it always came back to the bottles on the drainboard.

"Why, the poor thing just wants a lick of food!" the keeper said thankfully. "All it wants is an early breakfast."

The keeper began to move slowly, so as not to frighten the bird. He walked over and shut the outside door. Then he filled a bottle with sweet drink and held it out toward the hummingbird.

The hummingbird swirled down and fluttered over the bottle. It put its long tongue into the spout. It began to feed, right on the edge of the sink. Then it flew around in the middle of the room. It looked as if it wanted to see what else it could discover. At last it flew back to the edge of the drainboard.

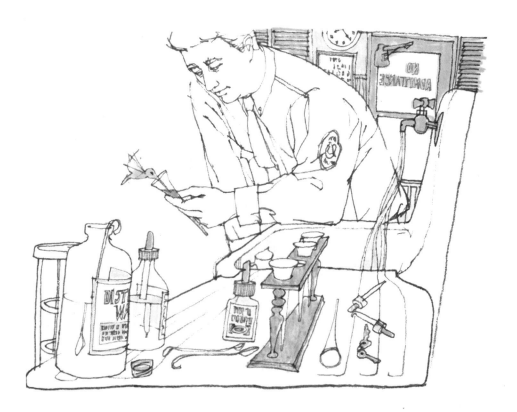

The hummingbird had eaten its lick of food. Now it lost all interest in bottle spouts. Instead it looked at the open faucet. It had never before seen water running out of a faucet. Still it was water, and hummingbirds like to bathe.

Zip! The hummingbird flew down and into the edge of the water. It beat its wings so fast they were almost invisible. Dip it went, in and out of the water.

The hummingbird had the finest of baths under the faucet. It was far better than the bath it always got in its cage. There the keeper just spattered water on the leaves of plants. The hummingbird had to bathe in the drops that fell from the leaves. At the sink it could bathe with plenty of water.

249

It was a while before the hummingbird lost interest in the fine bath. Then the keeper thought it was time for it to return to its cage. Could he interest the hummingbird in food again?

The keeper lifted the bottle from the edge of the drainboard. He backed slowly in the direction of the cage. The hummingbird followed him. It went into the bottom of the cage. Then the keeper shut the door.

After that the keeper always opened the door of that hummingbird's cage every morning. It flew straight to the edge of the sink for its breakfast. Then it had a bath while the keeper fixed food for the others.

The keeper was very proud. He was the only keeper in the zoo who had a pet hummingbird.

How to Tell the Top of a Hill

The top of a hill
Is not until
The bottom is below.
And you have to stop
When you reach the top
For there's no more UP to go.

To make it plain
Let me explain:
The one *most* reason why
You have to stop
When you reach the top—is:
The next step up is sky.

John Ciardi

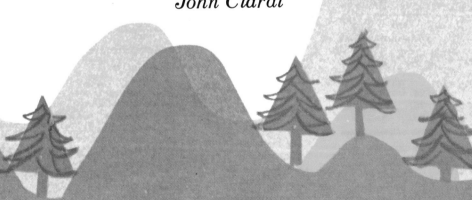